ABOUT THE AUTHOR:

Amelia Gregory is a publisher, art director, editor, graphic designer, writer, blogger, photographer, lecturer, climate activist and ceilidh caller who lives in East London, where she runs Amelia's Magazine (the website) and Amelia's House (the publishing company) out of her house. She is completely incapable of doing only one thing at a time.

interviews by Adam Sutcliffe, Ali Rodney, Amelia Gregory, Cari Steel, Chloe Stead, Katie Weatherall, Luisa Gerstein, Matt Bramford, Sabrina Morrison, Sally Mumby-Croft and Satu Fox

special thanks to Bruce Gregory for researching the technologies, Cari Steel for co-ordinating the writers, Ursula Gregory for sub-editing, and my printers Martin Darby and Alan Flack for their continuing support

edited, art directed and designed by Amelia Gregory

hardback first edition of 3000
published in December 2009 by Amelia's House
+44 7803 899643
www.ameliasmagazine.com
info@ameliasmagazine.com

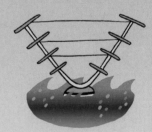

printed with vegetable based inks and eco-laminated in Kent, UK by Principal Colour
printed on Marazion, FSC approved paper from Fenner Paper
distributed by Central Books, orders@centralbooks.com

ISBN 978-0-9564095-0-8

Amelia's
anthology of
illustration

*featuring
renewable technologies
to prevent catastrophic
climate change*

a book to inspire creativity in the climate of change
by Amelia Gregory

published by **Amelia's House**

DEAR READER,

Welcome to my Anthology of Illustration. I hope that you will delve into these pages to discover a wealth of inspiration, from candid interviews with talented illustrators to aesthetically engaging imagery and exciting ways in which we can prevent catastrophic climate change. Where on earth did I chance upon such a combination? Well... for five years I produced a print magazine known as Amelia's Magazine, which provided a platform for up and coming artists of every description. Over the years I became more and more intrigued by the ability of artists to tell a story that cannot easily be related verbally – that of the challenges and possibilities we face if climate change continues unabated. Climate change is caused by our several hundred year long love affair with the concentrated energy found in cheap fossil fuels, which release huge amounts of carbon dioxide into the atmosphere when they are burnt, trapping heat inside the earth's atmosphere. For many hundreds of years before this humanity made use of renewable energy from the sun, moon and earth and once again these sources are being explored by some incredibly creative inventors. Illustrators are perfectly placed to make these – as yet unimplemented – renewable technologies tangible to a wider audience.

To find the 40 illustrators featured in this book I created an open brief on my Amelia's Magazine website, open for anyone to enter no matter how much or little experience they had. The only criteria in choosing the final contributors was the ability of each illustrator to answer the brief intelligently and imaginatively, show an interesting overall portfolio, and respond well to my art direction. Illustrators who have previously produced work for Amelia's Magazine* were shown preference for their continuing initiative. As a result the illustrators featured herein represent a wide mix of styles and experience – some are full time professionals who have been working in the industry for a few years, whilst some are still at college, just graduated or have yet to find their feet. Some may choose never to become full-time illustrators. It is after all, a difficult path to choose, and because this book is about and for illustrators, the interviews deliberately present a realistic picture of what it is like to work as an illustrator today. Each was asked to describe their relationship with computers and the internet, how climate change has affected both subject matter and approach, and the difficulties of finding jobs. Hopefully the very fact of appearing in this book will prove to other new creatives that if you work hard, promote yourself and take a risk you're likely to be rewarded, if not monetarily then cerebrally. And anyway, no one chooses to become an illustrator because they want to make lots of money.

Some facts really stood out from all the interviews. Helpful networks and friendships are critically important in what can often be a very lonely profession, either through finding a spot in a shared studio, or online, harnessing the power of social networking sites to speak with others all over the world. Collaborations are to be thoroughly recommended – both as a way of getting input from others and also for gaining more recognition. Promotion is paramount; get a professional looking website, use social media such as blogs, enter as many open briefs as possible, and engage with possible clients in clever ways. And it may be fun to do pretty designs, but the satisfaction of engaging with a thought-provoking subject is an even better feeling. One wonderful aspect of putting an open brief out on the internet is that I had submissions from all over the world, so this book features work from (amongst others) illustrators in Japan, Australia, South Africa, Scotland, Cyprus, Romania and Arkansas, USA. No matter where you are in the world, there is now the opportunity to work together.

For those worried about rapid climate change the "featuring renewable technologies to prevent catastrophic climate change" part of the book should help to alleviate your anxieties. And be cause for celebration and hope. For there are a lot of people out there trying to create a better future. Most of the featured technologies are remarkably simple, using similar principles in slightly different ways, so while it was impossible to cover every single variation in this book, all you have to do is let your imagination run wild – for example, imagine making energy from every type of kite that could ever take to the sky... and then stick a kite in the sea as well. However, what is striking is that so few inventors are able adequately to articulate their visions, as if the separation between art and science has become so exaggerated that no one can see the creative similarities any longer. Strange, because inventors are clearly incredibly, well, inventive people, but they often rely on illustrations to describe ideas that have yet to produce any real imagery of their own. It is staggeringly obvious, when trawling the internet, that the amount of interest generated for any one invention is in direct relation to the amount of inspiring representations available for it, and indeed the technologies that the illustrators liked the best were often those with an evocative name and a certain amount of available imagery already.

In researching each technology the internet inevitably became my best friend, and I quickly learnt a lot more science than I thought I would be able to digest. I detested science at school, perhaps because it seemed so uncreative, so was somewhat surprised to find that the basics are fairly easy to understand, and quickly got swept into the stories behind each idea. I've tried to make the descriptions as easy to understand as possible, so as long as you can get your head around the idea that 1MW (a million watts) can power approximately 1000 Western homes (according to levels of consumption of course), and 1GW (a billion watts) can power many times more, then you should be okay. Ultimately the technologies featured in this book are for the most part still fantasy so where possible I have checked with original sources, but I haven't included links to websites because some are barely legible and I expect the available information to change dramatically over the next few years. If your appetite is well and truly whetted I suggest you go and google the ideas for yourself – it's a whole fantastic world out there.

Sadly it became very apparent during my research that some technologies are very much favoured for investment, and typically they are those that could serve purposes other than merely supplying renewable energy, for instance the 'cleantech' solutions that have possible implementations for weapons or going into space. Perhaps inevitably these are preferred over, for instance, those that could provide easy, cheap and local sources of energy and fresh water for poor countries. It's clear that many things need to change beyond merely finding new ways to produce energy – no amount of clever technology will sort out the mess humanity has got itself into, especially if it just serves to perpetuate the global capitalist system that got us here in the first place. Without a radical shake-up green technologies will only provide a temporary band-aid for the underlying cracks in our current economic system, which is built on the concept of infinite growth. Of course this is inherently fallible because our precious planet is finite, and any resources will inevitably be exhausted one day – ultimately not much will change if fossil fuels are merely replaced with renewables and we continue to guzzle energy unabated. Yes, we might be able to float balloons in the stratosphere, catch the Gulf Stream in generators and tap heat from deep in the earth, but by definition nothing is forever renewable. If we cover the whole world with solar panels and turbines we would irrevocably alter delicate ecosystems and the very winds and tides that power the planet and make it what it is. Who knows, the results many centuries down the line could turn out to be as bad as our current love of fossil fuels.

The capitalist market system has been built on the massive gulf between the lifestyles and energy consumption of the very rich and the very poor, and if new technologies are developed and marketed under the same system we are doomed. There are surely no easy answers but many of the fabulously inventive and well-meaning ideas in this book will remain just that unless money is invested in making them a reality – and always with the possibility that they could fail. Rich investors are used to taking on the full risk of a project, only on the possibility of hitting the personal monetary jackpot, but this is clearly failing when it comes to providing affordable low-tech solutions, which no matter how effective are always passed over in favour of something hi-tech. And if power continues to be concentrated in the hands of the few the commodification of renewables will bring corruption just as the oil, gas and coal industries have. How can this be solved? Perhaps by a combination of ethical investors committed to ploughing money back into similarly useful projects, and of direct community ownership of an energy source. What is certain is that we must move away from centralised power networks towards community-owned and decentralised systems where technologies are shared. A direct relationship to an energy source is more likely to breed an understanding of its limits and a careful relationship to that supply.

Finally, it is a creative gift to be able to fantasise about the technologies in this book, and thoroughly exciting to know that in a few years some of them will inevitably come to pass and even become a normal part of our lives. Others will inevitably flounder and fail and some may turn out to be incredibly bad ideas after all, but right now we can't possibly know which – and that's the beauty of imagining the future. We have the ability to try and make it as brilliant as possible, both for our own selfish sakes and those that come after us. My dream is that some day this book becomes a relic of an age when many things were possible, similar to how we dreamed of space travel in the 1950's and the glorious age of computers during the 1970's. Except this time our fantasies will have flourished so beautifully that people will wonder what we were so worried about back at the turn of the 21st century.

Come, dream with me...

♡ Amelia x

CONT

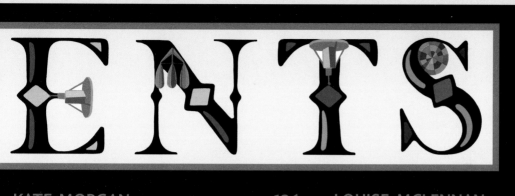

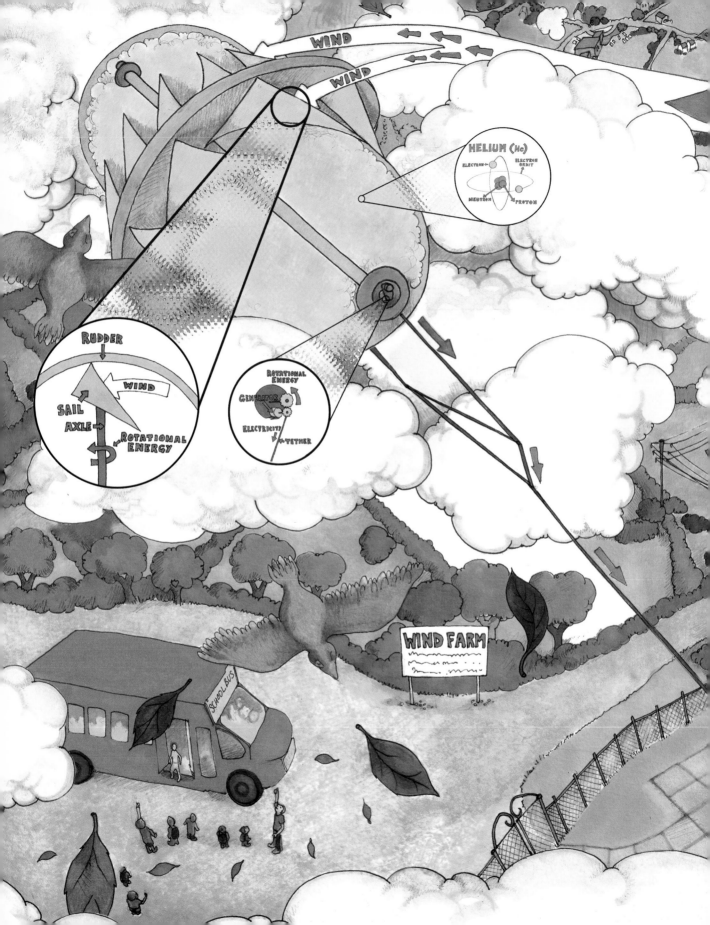

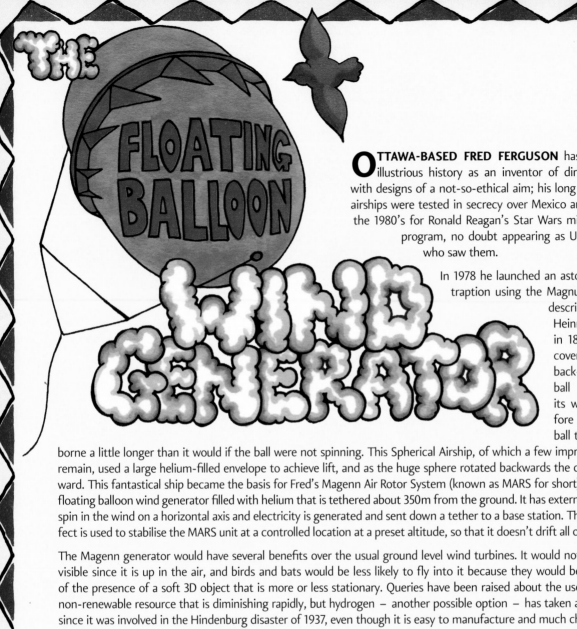

THE FLOATING BALLOON WIND GENERATOR

OTTAWA-BASED **FRED FERGUSON** has a long and illustrious history as an inventor of dirigibles, often with designs of a not-so-ethical aim; his long cigar-shaped airships were tested in secrecy over Mexico and Quebec in the 1980's for Ronald Reagan's Star Wars missile defence program, no doubt appearing as UFOs to those who saw them.

In 1978 he launched an astonishing contraption using the Magnus Effect first described fully by Heinrich Magnus in 1852, who discovered that the back-spin of a ball counteracts its weight, therefore allowing the ball to remain airborne a little longer than it would if the ball were not spinning. This Spherical Airship, of which a few impressive photos remain, used a large helium-filled envelope to achieve lift, and as the huge sphere rotated backwards the craft flew forward. This fantastical ship became the basis for Fred's Magenn Air Rotor System (known as MARS for short), a 30m wide floating balloon wind generator filled with helium that is tethered about 350m from the ground. It has external blades that spin in the wind on a horizontal axis and electricity is generated and sent down a tether to a base station. The Magnus effect is used to stabilise the MARS unit at a controlled location at a preset altitude, so that it doesn't drift all over the place.

The Magenn generator would have several benefits over the usual ground level wind turbines. It would not be so highly visible since it is up in the air, and birds and bats would be less likely to fly into it because they would be more aware of the presence of a soft 3D object that is more or less stationary. Queries have been raised about the use of helium, a non-renewable resource that is diminishing rapidly, but hydrogen – another possible option – has taken a very bad rap since it was involved in the Hindenburg disaster of 1937, even though it is easy to manufacture and much cheaper to use.

Fred is happy to use whatever lighter-than-air gases are available and is keen to point out that smaller versions of the turbine can be lifted filled with nothing more than air. He has a vision to manufacture small units, backpack-sized, that would be easy to carry, quick to erect and cheap (much like pop-up tents) – large turbines could be used for commercial energy provision and smaller ones could be deployed for disaster relief.

In 2008 the first large scale Magenn turbine was tested under various conditions, including its ability to stay safely anchored under the same weight load as five cars. It was proved to work. And if all this doesn't sound outlandish enough, there's always Twind, another 'captive balloon' system whereby two balloons with kites attached drive a winding mechanism to produce electricity. One can only hope the new story of blimps will progress towards a better outcome than that of the ill-fated zeppelin era.

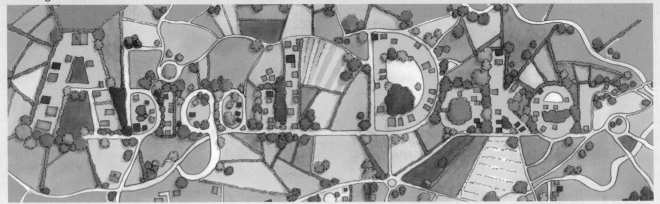

AT THE MOMENT ABI DAKER is in her studio, on the Mediterranean island of Cyprus, using the last dregs of a pen to colour in "....a very fluffy yeti." Apparently dried out pens are ideal for achieving this texture. "He doesn't have a name yet but," she assures me, "he is friendly, lives in an icy cave and drinks tea." The drawing will be coloured, scanned and volleyed between inboxes until it is considered ready for appearance in The Lost Sock, a children's book by Maltese writer Rita Antoinette Borg. At some point she will show it to as many children as possible for feedback. "They tend to point out crucially important things that an adult wouldn't even consider. For instance they wanted to see Santa in his workshop making computer games rather than the traditional toys I had drawn."

An amazing thing, a child's mind. It doesn't rain much in Paphos so whilst her young son Joseph is at school, Abi, fuelled up with coffee, will leave her little studio and head outside to sketch. Back in her image-covered workplace, illustrations will evolve in fine black marker, Pantone ProMarkers and watercolour before being scanned and reworked in Photoshop. "The nice thing about using Photoshop so early on is that it can give the client the opportunity to think of something they want added very late into the piece, without any need for the whole illustration to be reproduced."

Abi is currently contributing her talents to a local open studio event while working on five (gulp) assignments. In addition to the illustrations for the The Lost Sock she is also painting a family portrait in watercolour (no small feat), illustrating a wine label, designing menus for a bar and painting a mural in a pub "whose darts team swear they play better drunk."

"Some of the projects take longer than others and I'm always surprised by how easy it is to slot them in around one another. For example," Abi explains. "I often have to do illustrations to accompany newspaper or magazine articles which are less complex and take less time than my children's illustrations so they make a good break from a long term project. It's nice to have a slight change in what I'm doing because it stops me from getting bogged down."

Amazingly it was only a few years ago that this fine art educated mural painter even thought about pursuing illustration. It began with an idea for a character based on a toy monkey she had. "He was so full of personality that I had to bring him to life. I imagined him having all sorts of adventures when I wasn't looking." Inspired by reruns of the Simpsons, Abi attempted to give a cartoony quality to her hero. "I spent a lot of time experimenting with different media, but watercolour and pencils were too wishy washy and I found colouring on the computer too perfect. Eventually I bought a pack of ProMarkers and realised that they were the perfect medium for me; the colours are beautiful, it's easy to build up in layers, the effects on watercolour paper are incredibly clear, plus I can keep that hand-drawn feel." There is a downside though. "They're unbelievably expensive! My family keep urging me to try a different way of colouring illustrations, but ProMarkers are the best media I've found to help me get across on paper what's in my head... so they're worth every penny."

When Abi saw the brief for this book she thought immediately of her favourite book growing up, The Usborne Book of Knowledge. A much venerated children's guide to all things scientific, it brought all kinds of processes to life with clever and engaging illustrations, something which Abi is adept at doing herself. She is also particularly fascinated by landscapes. "The setting of a story can be the most crucial element in an illustration because it gives room to add a bit of depth to the character." The repeated accusations that turbines are an eyesore prompted Abi to depict the Floating Balloon Wind Turbine blending into its environment, with clouds and blowing leaves all included from a fascinating bird's eye view, a popular angle throughout her work. "It feels like quite an objective way to view the landscape because you can see how houses or patches of trees are grouped together. I like to emphasise how a landscape changes, for example I like to show the way that buildings move down the slope of a hill. Abi feels it is madness not to take advantage of the wind. "I had no idea just how many solutions people had been inventing. I hope people will keep tweaking them so that the dangers/expenses/complications are reduced and the technologies become more viable as widespread energy solutions."

Abi also drew her impression of a how humans could power their own gym equipment and provide energy. "My idea came from reading discussions about hamster wheel technology, an idea that is impractical for many different (and entertaining) reasons," Abi writes. She hit Wikipedia for information on treadwheels, which are described as "a form of animal engine typically powered by humans." Interestingly it also describes treadwheels thus: "originally a type of mill operated by a person treading steps of a wheel to grind grain, now designates a piece of indoor sporting equipment for running without moving any distance," which she feels illustrates the ridiculous position the modern world is now in, where a device that was formerly used to generate energy is now being used to get rid of energy. Abi explains how it is important to incorporate energy production into our physical daily life as much as possible because small changes are crucial to tackling the energy crisis. "Many people in the Western world are overweight these days and a large percentage are actively seeking to lose weight. The only way in which weightloss can be achieved is by burning off energy – effectively, wasting energy."

Ever the pragmatist, Abi points out that it must be difficult for decision makers to choose which technologies to back and at what point in their development. "Each technology I read up on seems so great, then you read about the next one and that's a great idea too. I think one of the hardest things about developing these technologies is that it only takes one accident or mistake to inspire a sea of negative press," she says. "I can remember seeing something on the news about wind turbines interfering with TV reception and that being a big negative against them. The only way these technologies will prevail is if we make sacrifices and unfortunately a lot of people aren't yet prepared to make personal sacrifices."

Abi may not need to. She doesn't own a TV and raises delectable marrows and squashes in the family allotment faster than they can be eaten. If her actions are anything to go by it looks like this island nation is definitely headed for greener pastures.

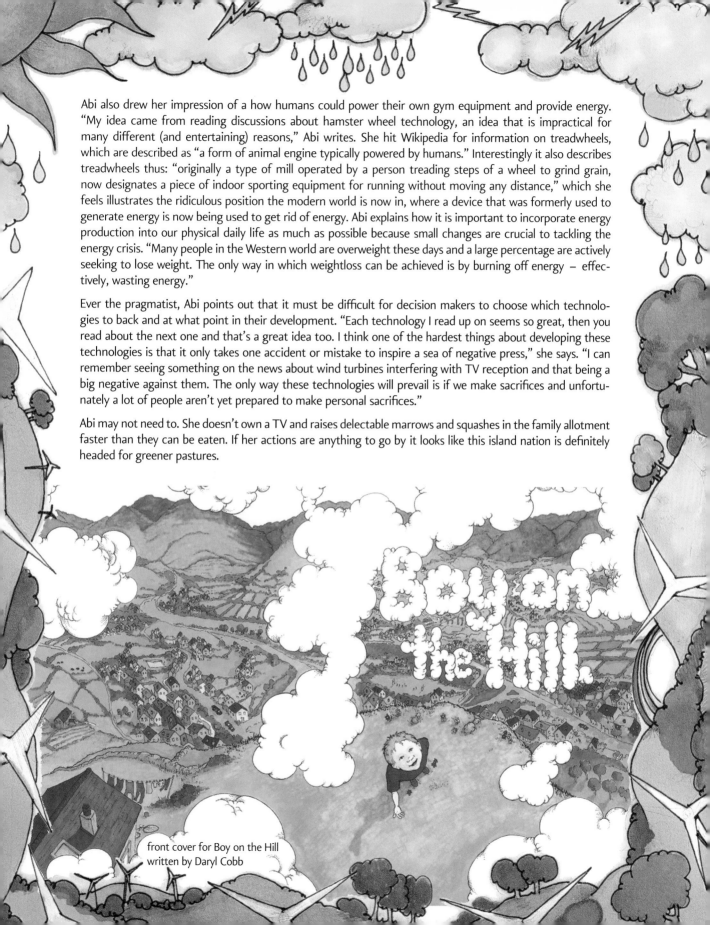

front cover for Boy on the Hill
written by Daryl Cobb

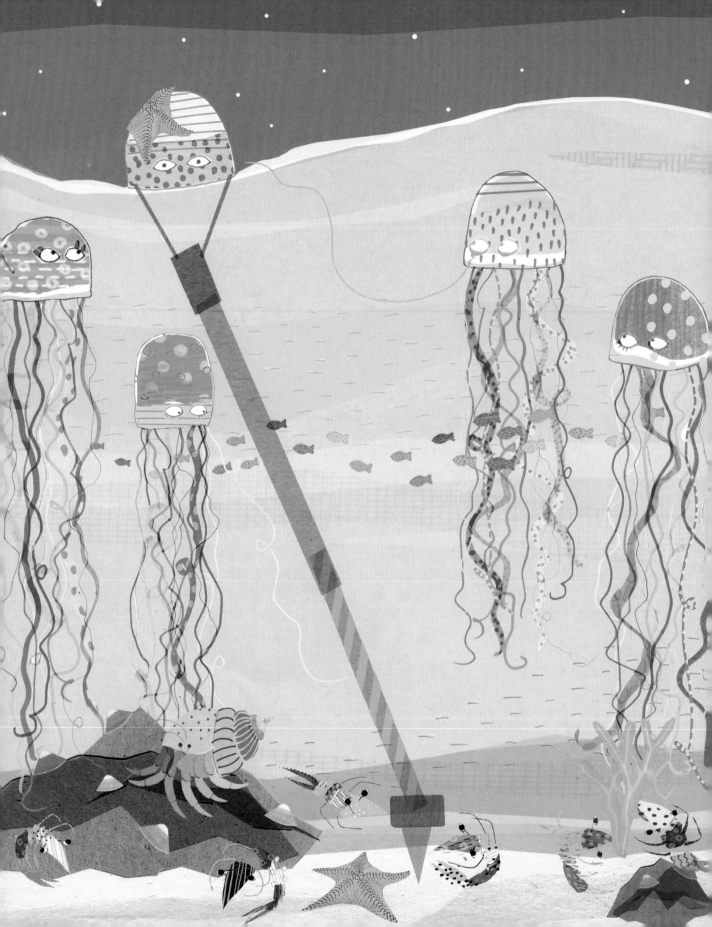

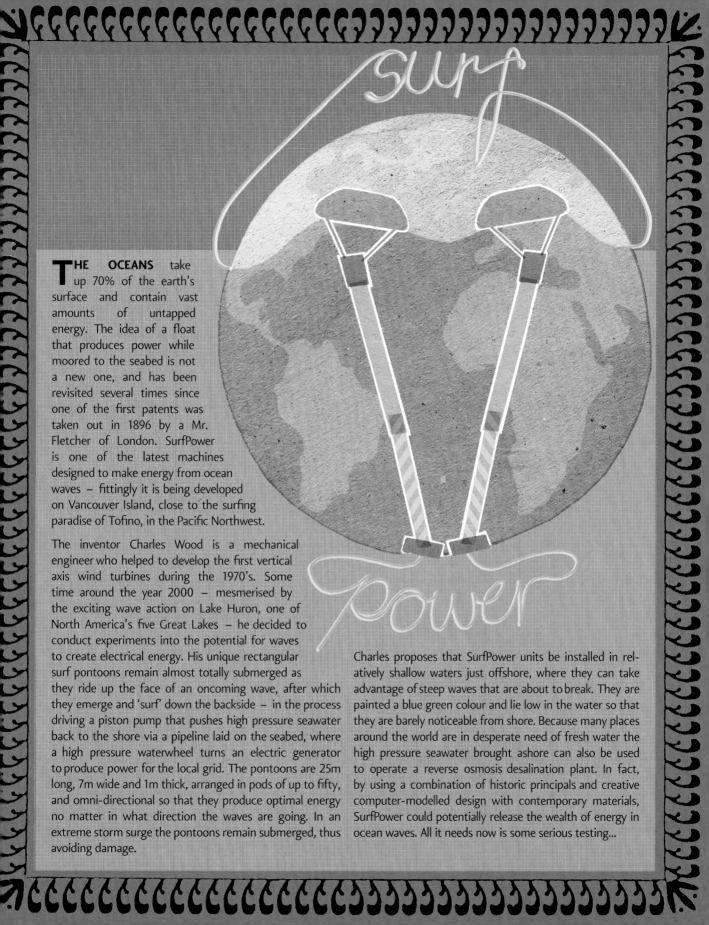

surf

power

THE **OCEANS** take up 70% of the earth's surface and contain vast amounts of untapped energy. The idea of a float that produces power while moored to the seabed is not a new one, and has been revisited several times since one of the first patents was taken out in 1896 by a Mr. Fletcher of London. SurfPower is one of the latest machines designed to make energy from ocean waves – fittingly it is being developed on Vancouver Island, close to the surfing paradise of Tofino, in the Pacific Northwest.

The inventor Charles Wood is a mechanical engineer who helped to develop the first vertical axis wind turbines during the 1970's. Some time around the year 2000 – mesmerised by the exciting wave action on Lake Huron, one of North America's five Great Lakes – he decided to conduct experiments into the potential for waves to create electrical energy. His unique rectangular surf pontoons remain almost totally submerged as they ride up the face of an oncoming wave, after which they emerge and 'surf' down the backside – in the process driving a piston pump that pushes high pressure seawater back to the shore via a pipeline laid on the seabed, where a high pressure waterwheel turns an electric generator to produce power for the local grid. The pontoons are 25m long, 7m wide and 1m thick, arranged in pods of up to fifty, and omni-directional so that they produce optimal energy no matter in what direction the waves are going. In an extreme storm surge the pontoons remain submerged, thus avoiding damage.

Charles proposes that SurfPower units be installed in relatively shallow waters just offshore, where they can take advantage of steep waves that are about to break. They are painted a blue green colour and lie low in the water so that they are barely noticeable from shore. Because many places around the world are in desperate need of fresh water the high pressure seawater brought ashore can also be used to operate a reverse osmosis desalination plant. In fact, by using a combination of historic principals and creative computer-modelled design with contemporary materials, SurfPower could potentially release the wealth of energy in ocean waves. All it needs now is some serious testing...

amy rhian

www.amyrhian.com

Bristol, UK

The perils of contemporary fantasy.

I've been working for Somerset Arts Week in my friend's studio, alongside wood and stone carvers, silversmiths and blacksmiths. Most of the artists were using traditional skills so I really stood out and one lady got really irritated. "Oh, well that's interesting" she said, obviously disliking my art. I just smiled sweetly, but she continued. "If I'm going to buy a piece of art I like it to look like what it's meant to. If everyone made art like you they'd never sell anything." Why did she even have to say that? I'm only just starting out!

One bedroom, one man and a dog.

I studied at the University of West England and then stayed on as a junior fellow, but that's just finished so I'm going to get stuck into my own stuff now. I've gone from having my own studio space to working in my one bedroom flat which I share with my dog and my boyfriend so there is inevitably loads to distract me, especially since I like everything to be tidy. I try to keep things professional by stopping for lunch breaks at a set time even though I'm at home.

Jersey V Bristol.

I come from the parish of St. Saviour on Jersey but moved to Bristol in 2004 to study. I miss being surrounded by the sea so I'm glad that there's a big river running through town. I don't miss the Jersey accent though, it's bloody horrible! It's got a twang of South African crossed with 'farmer'. I wish I had a Welsh accent; that would be great.

Process of work.

I'm really inspired by colour and pattern, and I love the work of the artist Hundertwasser. First I draw out the characters and other elements with pencils, then I cut out pieces of paper and construct each image before I scan them into the computer. Sometimes I work with felt tips too. It can be hard working on a tiny laptop screen but my relationship with my computer is pretty good. When I am in need of some fresh inspiration I take my dog for a walk around the woods.

The power of good literature.

My work tends to change depending on what I am reading. I'm interested in drug addiction, mental illness and autism. Two of my favourite authors are Charles Bukowski and Bret Easton Ellis; when I read hedonistic novels my work becomes instant, rough and messy. I also read a lot of fantasy aimed at younger readers, such as Harry Potter, the Philip Pullman series, some old Enid Blyton stories, contemporary fairytales by magic realist Francesca Lia Block and most recently the vampire stories of Stephenie Meyer. I tend to create fun, imaginative collages when I am immersed in these tales. To remind myself of methods of working I keep a journal about all the books I read so I can refer back to it for inspiration.

Collective parties and middle-aged American fans.

Lots of my illustrator friends have stayed in Bristol so there are plenty of people around. I've got two friends in particular who are both working illustrators and they're often at home on the internet too so I send them my work as I do it and they do the same for me. I'm also part of the Hot Soup art and music collective: we host multi-media parties once a month and are setting up a design agency. I use Twitter to promote my blog, which gets quite a few followers although I'm not entirely sure where they all come from. A lot of them appear to be middle age American housewives, which is awful! I'm also working on an artists' publishing project called Jovial Woods.

Tell us about your dancefloor.

Oh, my dancefloor piece, I'm quite pleased with that one. The illustration depicts a crystal dancefloor that generates electricity from movement. It can provide up to sixty percent of the electricity needed to power an eco friendly nightclub – I think there are only three of these dancefloors in the world at the moment and one is near Kings Cross in London. I originally wanted to include people in the forest reminiscent of the Bristol free party scene, but decided to use animals in the end. I much prefer to illustrate animals than people! For my main image I took inspiration from the idea of a phonemast

disguised as a tree so I've disguised the SurfPower machine as a jellyfish. Working on these illustrations made me think about all the day-to-day things I'm doing that could be used to produce power. Think of all that untapped energy generated in gyms! Why shouldn't people have to cycle five minutes to get that smoothie?

The future boils down to time and energy.

My ultimate aim is to support myself as a professional illustrator with my own studio. I'd love to get into sewing and making stuff but I guess starting out is always the most difficult part, isn't it? I see myself doing a bit of everything; editorial, stationery, packaging... I never thought about illustrating children's books before but quite a few people seem to be buying my work for their kids so that's a possibility too. It would be great to run some skillsharing courses that unite creative people from different disciplines. Basically success all boils down to how much time and energy you're willing to put into a project. Right now I'm open to all briefs so we'll just have to see whom I work with next!

www.anabotezatu.com

Romanian-born Ana Botezatu lives in the town of Cluj-Napoca, far from the snow-covered mountains of her childhood. "I don't want to sound like an old person but the winter here is not the same... what I miss most is the feeling when I woke to a certain light in the room and just knew the snow had come... big and thick and white; so heavy that the poor trees could barely hold it."

Ana acknowledges that it can be hard to make it as an illustrator in Romania, but she has been admirably proactive in finding opportunities on the internet to raise her profile, despite an aversion to social networking sites. "I don't have time for them and I don't really get their purpose." A ten square metre space forms her studio, doubling as an experimental exhibition space for her own and fellow artists' work. She prefers to work alone: "If the idea is personal I find it really hard to discuss with anyone, but this can make work a very lonely process." Ana therefore makes sure that she has short breaks to communicate with her fellow artists via her beautiful blog – a showcase for intricate pop-up sketchbooks, delicate watercolour experiments and numerous craft-based projects – and her soon-to-be web shop. "Everybody needs to hear feedback from

time to time. And I'm concentrating on creating a stable business so I have to stick my head out of my comfort zone." She is particularly proud of her presence on the Book By Its Cover website. "It's the best site for illustration – it actually made me want to become a serious illustrator so I was very flattered when they published my work." Some years out of college she is now starting to receive numerous, diverse commissions from those who've tracked her down.

Her unique handmade books were created in reaction to a stressful time "during a very rough moment in my life, a turning point." They were easy to transport when she was less settled and provide a handy reminder not to get too depressed. She's just got back from a holiday in Leipzig in Germany. "It's an amazing city with the most friendly museum I have ever visited, full of natural light. Every new place has a certain atmosphere, so I just let myself be filled with all the new information to inspire future works."

She tries to set a strict daily schedule for herself. "The morning starts with a coffee whilst I look over unfinished ideas. I then make a 'to do' list before starting work." Despite such organisation, inspiration often strikes at the most unexpected of times. "I'll be taking a rest when – suddenly – I'll start to draw something

BOTEZATU

Cluj-Napoca, Romania

unexpected." She's always embarked on some project or other, gleaning ideas from her life as she goes. "My work reflects what I'm going through, the people I know, the books I read, the places I go. Everything I include has touched me in a particular way." In the ultimate symbiosis Ana's art imitates her life, as her life feeds her art. "I can't imagine my life without creating art... and I guess that is what feeds me. A good day's work gives me enough energy to be happy in everything else."

Ana Botezatu was immediately drawn to the idea of kites as producers of energy because their iconic shapes reminded her of traditional Romanian storytelling. She decided to envisage them in the naïve style, depicting them as if at sea in another time. "I can see this beautiful technology being used in poor areas of Romania near the Black Sea or the Danube Delta."

Ana thinks it is impossible to ignore the visible damage our current lifestyle is causing to the planet. "I think one of the biggest problems facing our society is that we want too much from higher political forces like the state. But we ignore the possibilities that lie at the end of our fingertips, so I would like to encourage people to become responsible for their own actions and impact upon the environment." Ana's research into ways in which individuals can effect change threw up some terrifying facts of which she was previously unaware. She is particularly worried by the number of plastic bags used by a single person each year and – perhaps less well known – the huge volume of water required to flush away each visit to the toilet. "One environmental group I found tries to prevent this unnecessary consumption of water by encouraging people to pee in the shower!" And does she pee in the shower now? "Ah yes, well... you've caught me out on that one!" she admits. "It was always my secret pleasure, but now I feel entitled to do it... And hey, I don't mind admitting that I pee in the shower if it brings more honesty into the world." Indeed.

LADDERMILL

THE INVENTION OF THE KITE is credited to the Chinese several thousand years ago, and within a few hundred years the idea had spread around the world with, as ever, those at war being particularly quick to note its usefulness. Military powers soon adopted kites for sending messages with suspended lanterns, crossing over into enemy territory with the aid of ropes and for psychological warfare; frightening the enemy with spooky sounds from above, mimicking fireballs from the heavens and even dropping pamphlets onto prisoners of war, thus inciting them to riot. In 1944 the Japanese sneaked bomb-laden balloons across the sea to America via high attitude jet streams.

Now of course, kites are best known as a source of family entertainment on a windy hillside. However anyone who has had a kite yanked out of their hands on a very windy day will be aware of the immense power present above our heads. At the Delft University of Technology one impressively named Wubbo Ockels is currently testing his Laddermill technology, which aims to take advantage of this very concept by sending ladders of kites up to high altitudes and then bringing them back down again in a rotational motion.

An ex-astronaut (the first and only Dutch citizen to have been into space) who once sported a very fetching moustache, Wubbo describes how the kites used are a cross between regular kites and airplanes, thus named kiteplanes. A kite naturally sails off into the sky, but getting a kite back to ground requires a force to pull it down, whilst an aircraft requires engines to gain altitude but can glide back to the ground. The kiteplanes therefore combine the climbing characteristics of kites with the landing characteristics of aircraft – when they need to be reeled in they are angled so that they fall out of the sky like a glider. A large loop of kiteplanes ascending and descending creates a rotational movement that can be connected to a generator to produce energy. The kiteplanes need to be both large in surface area as well as light in construction weight and inflatable designs are being investigated.

Delft University have tested a 10m squared version of their kite machine and established that it can produce enough electricity to power ten family homes. The next step is to find backing so that the proposed technology to take the kiteplanes seriously skyward is not left languishing in the lab. The hope is that a loop of kiteplanes can ultimately fly up as high as 10km into the atmosphere, thereby taking advantage of increased wind speeds that carry hundreds of times more energy than on the ground. Some areas of the world are uniquely placed to harness such power in an effective way; Britain, the Netherlands and Denmark are particularly 'wind rich'. It is estimated that these huge Laddermills could generate approximately 100MW each, enough to power a hundred thousand homes.

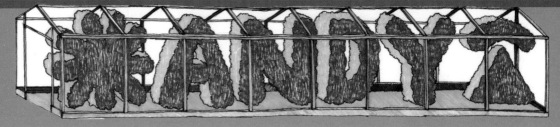

"My drawings have always been intricate but they're definitely getting more detailed," says multimedia artist Andrew Merritt. Their complexity is down to reflexive thinking combined with a hand drawn style. "With a pen you can immediately get out what you've got in your brain, whereas it's a bit slower on a computer because it's not so natural." These days he's wondering, in fact, what he can best use a computer for. "Maybe I need to think about how I can use my drawing for animation..." he muses.

Andrew studied graphic design at Brighton University before graduating in 2003. "It gives another element to my work," he explains. "If I had studied illustration alone I would have just been an illustrator – but now I'm an illustrator and loads of other things as well!" The 'other things' that Andrew speaks of are his work within the disciplines of architecture and sculpture. Due to his education in design he feels more able to answer briefs than many artists. "I like the challenge of trying to come up with an idea to fit a brief. I guess that's why I got into the world of creating public sculptures rather than private ones." Which came first, the sculptures or the illustration? "Because I often need to present my ideas first I have to draw my sculptures before I make them. It seemed like the next logical move to push the illustrations themselves."

Andrew recently completed a joint commission called CarPark for the London Festival of Architecture. "The idea was to imagine what we do after the demise of the car, so we took the roof off a scrap vehicle and raised it up on wooden supports, then filled the engine with flowers and put a miniature pond in the boot." Apparently it was a big hit with the kids. Andrew's desire to bring nature into the city is an underlying inspiration and theme for much of his work, "I'm interested in how humans can be more accommodating to the natural world. Nature is good for the soul." He delights in growing vegetables on his "ridiculously long" balcony. "I was really busy this year so they all died, but I still got quite a lot: runner beans, tomatoes, courgettes and peas."

A solitary worker, Andrew prefers the freelance lifestyle. "I have my own fixed ideas so I just like to get on with making them happen." And anyway, a healthy mix of sculpture and illustration provides a diverse working environment. "I create illustrations at home but because sculptural work tends to be onsite it means that I get out and meet different people. I like that balance." But he doesn't hang out with other illustrators. "I'm quite insular, and I don't want to get overwhelmed with too many trendy ideas because then I might lose sight of what is important to me. I'm more interested in talking with people about things I don't know much about... like fungi."

He often collaborates with architects. For the Barbican's Radical Nature exhibition the experimental architectural collective EXYZT erected a fully functioning wheat mill in the middle of rundown Dalston in East London and Andrew produced a detailed imagined dreamscape of the area around the Dalston Mill. His vision of sustainability featured "skyscrapers covered with plants, a massive greenhouse, a hotel for bugs, a makeshift beach and a multi-level Ridley Road Market. The buildings balance on a scaffolding structure held up by cranes."

In Bethnal Green Andrew worked with French humanitarian charity Médecins du Monde to design a medical clinic for refugees without access to the healthcare system. During this project he was introduced to the prominent architect Richard Rogers, which proved to be a major influence in the direction of his work. "Ever since then my drawings and sculptures have become more architectural in feel."

On the subject of architecture Andrew is passionate, particularly if the building in question was built in Georgian times. "They were well made and the proportions just look so right." He thinks we should be reusing and redeveloping the buildings we already have rather than starting afresh. "They're knocking down all these amazing warehouses on the harbour in Ipswich. People would love to live in them; it's as if no one has learnt a thing." He is full of derision for "big iconic buildings" of the type that pepper central London, "It's all do to with money and ego," and is convinced that even the most unlovable bits of architecture are capable of new life. "I want to turn multi-storey car parks into vegetable patches," he declares. "An ugly building can be transformed with a bit of imagination." He's even considered how the crops would receive enough sunlight to grow; "sun tunnels and big mirrors." And of course his friends the fungi are never far away. "At the very centre of the building it will be dark and moist which is perfect for mushrooms." His only worry is that someone will get there with his idea first. "I don't see why it couldn't happen... now that cars are being pushed out of cities. Soon these car parks will be useless."

MERRITT

For EcoLabs Andrew drew four possible future scenarios, as envisaged by the ecologist David Holmgren (who urges us to act as stewards of the earth via a community led transition). The rain-catchers are part of a project which is already under way for a school in Hammersmith – using the same motion sensors found in the latest car screen wiper technology, they open whenever it starts to rain and capture storage water as well as offering shelter to those beneath. A sense of function combined with fun is evident throughout Andrew's work. "For the main illustration I imagined a caterpillar walking, so I combined the bright colours and strange forms of caterpillars with that of a pleasure pier," he explains. And thus a new multi-functional wave energy provider is born.

Future Scenarios for EcoLabs Climate Roadshow

THE first burst of wave energy inventions occurred from the late 1800's onwards, with no less than thirty US patents taken out between 1870 and 1910 for pier-based wave machines featuring assorted bobbing floats and flapping mechanisms. One concept that was granted a patent at the turn of the century looks remarkably similar to the recently-developed Danish Wave Star Energy machine – the patent diagram shows multiple floats on levers that drive pistons filled with compressed air.

With extensive coastlines bordering stormy oceans and multiple offshore wind turbine farms already in place it is perhaps not surprising to discover that Denmark is amongst the world's most advanced countries in developing wave power. In 2000 Niels and Keld Hansen – two brothers from a small seaport on the Jutland peninsula – were inspired by a love of sailing to invent a machine that obtains a steady supply of energy from waves rolling towards the shore. Their machine features a long backbone that is towed out to sea on a barge and fixed to the seabed, where it is orientated in the dominant wave direction. Dangling from the central section is a series of arms that end in enormous floats that bob up and downwards one at a time as each wave passes, thereby exploiting its entire length. One of the biggest problems of technology at sea is possible damage from the elements, so when waves exceed a critical height the floats are automatically retracted from the water until the storm waves pass.

Per Resen Steenstrup discovered the brothers' idea in 2003 whilst searching for a wave energy technology that was capable of competing in cost and productivity with offshore wind turbines, and has since put two working machines into practice. The first scaled-down model has remained in continuous operation for several years whilst surviving numerous storms fully intact, making it arguably the most successful wave energy prototype currently in use. The second version was inaugurated in late 2009 in the North Sea off Hanstholm. Designed as a showcase for the COP15 climate talks in Copenhagen it is a 40m long test section of a full scale plant, with only two arms on each side featuring floats that measure a massive 5m in diameter. The final proposed unit will be capable of dealing with 5m waves and produce 6MW, making it comparable with large offshore wind turbines. However, operating and maintenance costs should be far less because all working machinery is kept at a low level. The energy found in waves is much denser than in wind and there is less fluctuation because waves diminish much less abruptly, continuing for several hours when the wind drops and thus making wave power much more predictable. For a constant supply of electricity it therefore makes good sense to combine wind and wave power installations, a fact that hasn't escaped the canny Per.

Wave Star Energy are very keen to make sure that their machine is constructed with the lowest carbon footprint possible, it is painted with non-toxic paints and biodegradable oil flows through its hydraulic systems. Painstaking observations of the area below the machine reveal that the shady environment has become popular with wildlife, with strong seaweed growth attracting fish and happy lobsters gathering at the legs of machine.

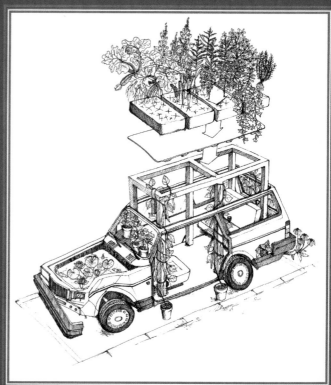

SHE'S an illustrator who enjoys watching crap telly whilst eating fish and cheese, although probably not all at the same time. She dreams of moving to San Francisco. "I'll live in a log cabin that I've built with my boyfriend and I'll make a living from illustration and art." She's an inveterate gossip who ignores the phone if she's not in the mood and admits to the occasional surly mood. She enjoys being in the full flow of work, deep in ideas and theories – but is equally happy far away from work, camping or at a reggae dance. If she wasn't an artist she'd definitely be doing something outside. "Maybe I'd be a horticulturist." Welcome to the complex world of multi-media artist Anna Beam.

WHAT INFLUENCES YOU?

I've only recently become confident enough to admit that I was raised on a healthy diet of science fiction, and that's had a big impact on my subject matter and imagery. Sci-fi novel covers, film posters and old Star Trek episodes have all influenced the colours I use. These days I find myself fascinated by conspiracy theories and religion... both of which can read like science fiction. I'm reading Robert Anton Wilson's Cosmic Trigger, The Final Secret of The Illuminati, which is taking me into the scary territory of totally whacky theories. He's such a good writer that I find myself getting seduced into a place where it becomes impossible to be objective and I suddenly find myself thinking "yeah man, I can totally see how Spock is a 20th century manifestation of the peyote cactus's plant spirit." I'm also really into the futuristic designs of avante-garde 60's collective Archigram. Their use of colour and typography gives me heart palpitations.

WHO INSPIRES YOU?

I like a lot of the work coming out of San Francisco, such as that of Daniel Tierney. What I've seen is colourful, witty and joyous. I like the way that Trenton Doyle Hancock constructs artworks out of cloth, paper and found objects as well as paints and I am inspired by the way that artists such as Maya Hayuk and Boo Ritson are able to transcend genres. They prove that lazy categorisations can be ignored.

IS MUCH OF YOUR WORK HAND DRAWN?

I still haven't fully come around to the idea of drawing on the computer. But then I'm not a total traditionalist; I doubt many illustrators are these days. The stuff that I'm working on right now is made up from separate flat and 3D constructed components which are photographed and then put together in Photoshop, so I suppose I am using the computer as a drawing tool which I've got to admit is pretty fun. I was raised in a family of PC users and was indifferent to computers until I got a Mac. Now I'm a total snob, probably similar to other Mac users. Mac way or the highway, man.

WHAT MATERIALS DO YOU WORK WITH?

I'm a big fan of gouache and I use lots of paper, some of it found. My background is in craft embroidery so I use cloth and stitch as drawing materials in my work; I aim to get to a point where I'm comfortable in using any kind of material to draw with. I particularly admire how the artist Jessica Stockholder fills entire exhibition spaces with seemingly incongruous 'stuff' that she calls paintings. I'm still at an early stage in my career so I expect my style will change and I guess that's inevitable – something to be embraced as part of the whole cohesive, flowing timeline of work. I keep a sketchbook of colours that I collect, kind of like a stamp collector's book. It's full of fabric, string, photos, bits of coloured plastic (from the beach is best), CD covers, scraps of rusty metal and broken car lights. I tried preserving the colour of live flower petals by laminating them, but that was no good: they just went mouldy. And the boxes that fruit and veg come in are an underrated source of cool colours and typography.

Manchester, UK

DO YOU JUGGLE
CREATING ART WITH ANOTHER JOB?

Yeah, I work part time as a greengrocer from a busted old caravan held together with bungees. I get to snack on fruit all day and talk to customers about what they're making for dinner, which is fun. I'm trying to find some other more artistic jobs, both paid and unpaid, but if the truth be known I enjoy having a job that has nothing to do with art. When a project is in full swing I tend to get obsessive about working and forget to have a social life, so having another job forces me to crawl out from inside my head, do a different task and hang out with people who have other interests.

HOW DO YOU WORK?

Ah, to have those expansive studios of art school once again! I'm sitting at a chipboard desk against an upturned bed that I use as a pinboard, in the second bedroom of our little flat in Hulme, Manchester. Sometimes I work on the floor which hurts my knees after a while. I've been warned that it could give me varicose veins, but it means I can spread my materials all around me and because I'm short I get a better view. I only recently left university, so I'm in the process of working out if it's better to work from home or have a studio. I wake up early and start working pretty much right away while the coffee's still brewing, and by ten or noon I'm in the swing of things. Then all of a sudden I have to unplug my creative side and go to work or go buy more cat litter... the rest of life has a habit of taking over at times. On a really good day I can work all day and into a good portion of the night.

WHAT'S GOING ON IN YOUR ILLUSTRATIONS?

In the Appalachians entire mountaintops are blown off to get at cheap seams of coal and I wanted to imagine what the residents would do if they wanted to reconstruct the landscape as it once was. Huge geodesic greenhouses are built to fit the original topography of the mountain and serve as nurseries for indigenous plant saplings that are presently having trouble regrowing. Once the trees are too big to be munched, claw-like kinetic powered heli-machines lift the trees out and transport them to the spot where they're to be replanted. Blowing up the top of a mountain produces a lot of rubble and waste that is dumped into the valleys, blocking up the waterways. The purple pyramids are temporary community-run brick-making factories to quarry stone that wasn't meant to be there in the first place. And I designed my logo for Hulme Community Garden Centre with workshops, volunteer and family days in mind. Entering the centre is like finding a secret garden within the bustling city.

CAN YOU TELL US ABOUT THE TECHNOLOGY YOU CHOSE?

Tidal Sails seemed quite unique amongst a lot of the other new technologies because of its accessibility. They can be made from pre-existing materials which would make them cheaper to manufacture and hopefully developing countries could install them more easily. And they don't need to be fixed to any surface, meaning less impact on the marine ecosystem.

HOW CAN WE LIVE A LESS ENERGY INTENSIVE LIFE?

The less energy we generate to make green technologies possible the better, and because the Tidal Sails are so resourcefully simple and elegant it made me think about what it would be like to generate less waste. If we were to work less, demand less energy and generally lead our lives at less of a rush then of course not only would we produce less waste but we'd be living at a slower pace of life and could take more time to appreciate how truly valuable the world around us is.

GENERATOR: STORES KINETIC ENERGY FROM SAILS AND SENDS IT TO A POWER STATION ON THE SURFACE

FLOATATION TANK: DEVICE CAN STAY SUBMERGED WITHOUT HAVING TO BE INSTALLED ON THE OCEAN FLOOR

OUTER BODY

PULLEY: REELS IN THE SAILS, COLLECTING ENERGY FROM THEIR MOVEMENT

BARRIER: STACKS SAILS IN FRONT OF THE PULLEY UNTIL THE CURRENT CHANGES AND THEY'RE PULLED THE OPPOSITE WAY.

SAILS: BY BEING STRUNG BETWEEN TWO ENDPOINTS ALLOWS THE DEVICES TO BE MADE TO ALMOST ANY LENGTH ACCORDING TO LOCATION

WHAT'S NEXT FOR YOU?

I'm in the middle of working on a project about future dystopias. What a contrast, eh?! I've got the four riders of the apocalypse camped out on my living room floor, which is cool because I'm intrigued by the intertwining relationship of dystopia and utopia. Should we return to a more natural and simplistic way of life, or do we push technology to its limits in an attempt to sustain our current lifestyles? What will ultimately make us happier?

TIDAL SAILS

Imagine sailor Are Borgeson racing his boat in a regatta: the wind is behind him and his spinnaker is up, but he can't move because the tidal current against him is so strong. And so he thinks, 'what if I just flip my boat upside down and use the sails to catch the currents beneath me?' Of course he didn't, because then he would've capsized, but thus the idea for Tidal Sails was born. In 2004 the company was founded in Haugesund on Norway's southwest coast, in a region – somewhat ironically – more used to supporting the offshore oil and gas industries.

Are's patented idea is simple. String some cables diagonally across a tidal stream at the correct angle and attach a series of underwater sails to them. As the tide pulls the sails the cables are unwound and power is generated. When the tide reverses the sails pull the cables back. Because of their simple design Tidal Sails would be cheap to manufacture and maintain, and the visual impact would be virtually nil since they are kept underwater and out of sight. They would be slow moving, thereby leaving wildlife free to carry on as usual, and the amount of power that could be captured is proportional to the area of the sails and so could be very large.

But of course all new ideas have to be tested. Are is certain that the system can cope with floating debris since the Tidal Sails hang freely in the water, but it is possible that the cables and sails will oscillate wildly in the tidal current. Perhaps this in itself can be used to create power? Only a serious trial of the Tidal Sails will tell...

CURRENT

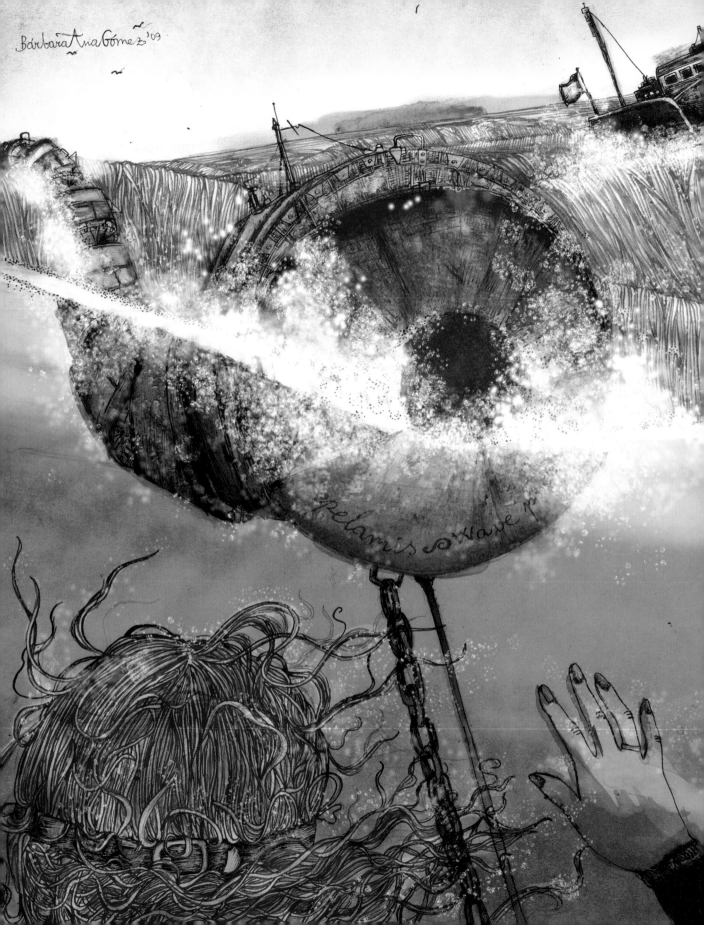

PELAMIS PLATURUS *is a venomous yellow-bellied tropical sea snake that prefers shallow inshore waters and avoids the Atlantic (too cool). Pelamis is also the name of a snake-like wave machine that is much larger, does not have a yellow belly and prefers the Atlantic.*

The current Pelamis prototype consists of four long bright red steel cylinders linked by three hinged sections. It measures 140m long (the equivalent of five train carriages), 3.5m wide and is moored so that it swings head-on to the arriving waves, causing the cylinders to move up and down and side to side. The motion at the joints is captured by pistons which drive high pressure oil through turbines situated inside the sections and the electricity is then sent via cables down to the seabed and onshore to the grid. The long thin Pelamis lie low in the water, thus avoiding the most damaging of storm waves, and the resistance of the joints can be altered to take maximum advantage of the power available at any one time.

Pelamis Wave Power, based in Scotland, has been developing their device since 1998 and installed the world's first commercial wave farm 5km off Aguçadoura on the northern coast of Portugal in 2008. These three units were together capable of providing power for 1000 family homes and it is anticipated that a 30MW Pelamis wave farm comprising forty machines covering a square kilometre of ocean could provide enough power for 20,000 homes.

Unfortunately the Pelamis concept has several problems. The joints are subject to extraordinarily strong forces as they are slammed back and forth out at sea, and when problems occur the entire assembly must be towed into port for repair. When this happens, no power is produced and large costs are incurred. Just months after being installed, the Portuguese machines were taken ashore and have not been reinstated.

Not only this but a single Pelamis device contains around 700 tonnes of steel, which is approximately three times as much raw material as that needed to build offshore wind turbines that deliver the same amount of power. However, the developers remain optimistic, believing that teething problems always arise with new technologies. An even bigger (180m long) version of the Pelamis machine is currently under construction for deployment off the coast of Orkney.

wave power

www.barbarana.es

barbara ana gomez

BARBARA ANA GOMEZ was born in Madrid and studied advertising and graphics before becoming... a graphic designer in the advertising industry. "Unfortunately my job soon became very boring so I came to London in search of inspiration and because this is the centre for arts in Europe," she explains. "Competition here is huge but I wanted the motivation to be the best." She did a part-time illustration course at the London College of Communications and is now making a living in freelance graphic design, working for Fortnum & Mason as well as designing packaging labels for the National Portrait Gallery, but she would give up graphic design for illustration in a shot. "With graphic design I always have to think about the target of the piece and how people will look at it, whereas illustration is more personal," she muses. "I feel as though I work more freely when I'm illustrating, but maybe that's because I haven't had a commission yet so I'm just drawing whatever I want!"

Barbara's illustrations are the antithesis of sleek graphic design. To achieve an antiqued texture sheets of paper are immersed in the bath with hot tea or coffee, left for a few hours and then hung out to dry. "And then you have to clean the bath because it also gets quite 'antiqued'," she laughs. She prefers to work exclusively on A3 paper. "By working big I give myself space to draw details such as an eye or a flower." Composition comes first, then coloured areas are filled in with the subdued tones of Winsor & Newton inks (a present from her boyfriend) before the image is scanned into the computer. "I can't live without Photoshop to fix mistakes."

Barbara chose to illustrate Pelamis, which uses the motion of surface waves to create electricity. What is the difference between attitudes to the environment in England and in Spain? "In Spain there are a lot of people concerned about the environment, but if you ride a bike to work you're seen as a hippy," she explains. "Here it's not uncommon for city boys to use bikes." She confesses that the initial attraction to the brief was a purely aesthetic one. "I thought I could make a beautiful image from the look of water, foam and floating hair." Barbara brings Pelamis to life with a perspective that juxtaposes the huge figure of a girl in front and a tiny industrial looking boat behind. "I was hooked on the TV series Lost when I drew this so I was feeling quite dramatic. I imagined how overwhelming it would be to come across this huge metallic machine by surprise, making strange noises as it's hit by the powerful waves." In this fledgling narrative she hasn't yet decided whether the girl has come from the boat to investigate the machine for the first time (having spent years studying how it works), or whether she is trying to hide from someone on the boat. "It was kind of hard to get the proportions right but this is the first time I've used such a dramatic perspective and I love how it came out." Did Barbara know about the testing of Pelamis off Portugal? "Yes, but I wasn't aware that they might have had problems," she says. "I hope that they are trying to improve it and will re-launch it in the future."

Barbara is working on a series called Freak Show based on a book of "amazing antique photographs" that she is re-interpreting in her own style. How else does she get inspiration for self-motivated illustration? "I look for competitions because then I have a brief. I also love to draw images inspired by music, so sometimes I take lyrics and draw something from them." A few years ago she produced a collection of images for the album cover of a Spanish folk-rock band and at LCC she made a long scroll inspired by Bowie's Space Oddity, on which she tried to communicate the feelings of the song with drawing and calligraphy. Ongoing work involves translating the lyrics of songs from Radiohead and American band The National, and background music is essential to get her in the right mood for work. "If I'm drawing something happy then I put on upbeat music, such as Vampire Weekend, Phoenix, Throw Me The Statue or 90's Britpop, but if I'm drawing something dark or emotional then I put on Arcade Fire, Fleet Foxes or Bon Iver."

She tries to keep in contact with fellow students from her course, and goes with friends to gallery openings and private views where she is able to meet and network with other artists over a drink or two. "I draw all the time, send out postcards, update my website, upload my work to online portfolios and enter competitions. I do anything I can find. Web communities are great for chatting to other people about your work." She gets the addresses for publishers, magazines and illustration agencies from the Writers' & Artists' Yearbook, from the internet and from people she knows. "As for self promotion," she declares, "you can find me on deviantART, Amateur Illustrator, Coroflot, Computerlove, Creativepool and ArtBistro. Every time I find a new website I sign up." Take note, burgeoning creatives.

WHEN designing something it's always a good idea to look first at how nature does things. Where then to look for the perfect design of an object that spins in the wind? A sycamore seed! British aeronautical designer David Sharpe has designed a giant sycamore seed shaped wind turbine named – somewhat appropriately given his background – the Aerogenerator. In practice this looks like a huge V-shaped TV aerial, spinning atop a fixed vertical shaft. As the wind blows the vanes of the seed spin...

David claims that this design could be used to make far larger wind turbines than we currently build – because size matters. Wind speed rises with height and power rises eight-fold for every doubling of wind speed. Do the maths; you want to be high high up baby. The trouble is that most standard wind turbines consist of three blades rotating on a horizontal axis, and as the blades get longer the stress increases. The same is true of standard vertical axis 'egg-whisk' wind turbines: repeated flexing of very large blades leads to failure. So there's a finite limit to size.

However, the clever Aerogenerator machine spins from the base, so most of the weight is kept at the bottom and all the machinery is low down and easy to get to. Stress is reduced so it should be possible to build a very large turbine, possibly up to 144m high, and generating 9MW, far more than standard wind turbines are capable of producing. Of course it would very likely put the NIMBYs in a colly-wobble if a gigantic Aerogenerator was built on land, but the aim would be to place them unobtrusively several kilometres out to sea, disturbing no-one but the giant octopi and the odd passing ship.

Tests of a model Aerogenerator at the renewables technology testing centre in Northumberland confirm that it works, possibly even at faster speeds than conventional turbines, so an excited bunch of people have now come together to try and make this dream machine a reality. The NOVA project's declared aim is to generate a gigawatt of power (that's the equivalent of several large power stations) from several Aerogenerators by 2020.

CHRIS COX

www.papercaves.com

"I LIKE TO CREATE MAGICAL LITTLE WORLDS," says Chris Cox. He is certainly adept at evoking an inviting fairytale universe. Who wouldn't want to get into the canoe that his characters old man Grayson and youngster Kirk are travelling in, and join them on their journey through the lakes that wind between the secret mountains, navigating an unseen path. "I like making illustrations that you want to touch," he laughs.

Chris is fastidious about timekeeping and goes to great lengths to ensure punctuality for his interview, arriving twenty minutes early. Thankfully, he is prepared for the possibility of mismatched arrivals with a well thumbed copy of Haruki Murakami's The Wind-Up Bird Chronicle to keep him company. "It's a surreal account of an unemployed bachelor who meets a series of bizarre characters while searching for his cat. It's true escapism, I become totally absorbed in the characters." He has taken the day off from his job as a designer at the digital creative agency Thin Martian to talk about the art he creates in his spare time. Cartoon-like digital illustrations produced with innovative software paradoxically depict the most natural of subjects and settings; woods, mountains, boats and rivers. Many of the illustrations appear light hearted and whimsical but look closer and a shadow of darkness becomes apparent. From concept to creation Chris is powered by escapism. Where does this vivid imagination come from? "I doodled a lot as a child," he says "I used to make my own comics full of heroes and robots. I remember one featured a pair of robots who were fascinated by the fact that they were robots! And I liked collecting things as well. I still hoard stuff." Inevitably he watched a lot of cartoons. "Transformers, Mysterious Cities of Gold, Ghostbusters – I was the perfect child for all the toy agencies."

He took his blossoming artistic streak to the University College of Creative Arts in Farnham to study Graphic Communication and joined not one, but two bands. As he explains, "Hikikomori Broadcast featured classical violin arrangements alongside indie guitar. I am aware that it sounds like the most pretentious thing ever!" It takes a lot of prompting to reveal the name of his other band: Tatsunoko's Bear. Paid gigs not being forthcoming he soon turned his sights back to design under the name Paper Caves, "because I like making landscapes and environments using collage and hand made techniques."

He scans as many textures as possible. "I photographed an apple to be the hat of one of my characters because I felt that he needed it." A similarity to the world of the Moomins is no accident. "I would count (Moomins illustrator) Tove Jansson as one of my major influences." Kite ladders are one of the renewable technologies that Chris would most like to see used. "I think kite ladders and underwater technologies are beautiful, like gliders that can produce kinetic energy from the wind and waves," he explains. "So I built a whole illustration around how I imagined the type of community that uses this technology would live. Grayson and Kirk have been out fishing when they stumble across this world by accident, a bit like in The Lion, The Witch And The Wardrobe." He hopes they will live on in animated form sometime soon.

Two of Hearts for Amelia's Magazine Shelter Card Quilt

Chris had conflicting feelings about the Aerogenerator. "I like the premise of such a futuristic technology but it is so huge that I found it quite daunting to figure out the size." The huge octopus wraps his tentacles around the massive machine in what appears to be a hug. It took two days of intensive work to get it right. "When I get into my work I don't do anything else, especially when I am enjoying it."

Living in Southgate in North London is ideal for Chris because of its proximity to greenery, which is where he goes to escape. For one memorable commission he recalls running around in the woods with his girlfriend. "We did some stop motion photography of characters running down a path and straight into a tree." He put the whole thing together afterwards in motion graphics software.

Chris is eager to experiment as much as possible with his illustration, and has plans in the pipeline to photograph – on a good quality camera – handmade dioramas based on classic kids' cartoons. In the meantime he networks on Twitter and follows briefs when he needs a bit of focus. Eventually he would love to do more children's illustration, citing Quentin Blake – who illustrated Roald Dahl's books – as a major inspiration. "Actually, at university I created a children's book out of card, acetate and rubber bands, " he reveals, "and that's what started me off on my present style of working." So if he created a book for children and did the illustration, would someone else write the story? "No!" he laughs, "I would do it all!" Just another feather in his cap then, but Chris Cox makes it seem so effortless.

SOLAR CONCENTRATING TOWERS look like something out of a sci-fi movie, light flashing in bright rays from hundreds of smart mirrors (known as heliostats) skywards to a boiler full of molten salt at the top of a tower forty stories high. The principle is akin to setting alight a piece of paper with a magnifying glass angled towards the sun, except on a vastly bigger scale. Whenever energy is needed water is pumped through the insulated tanks that contain the heated salt mixture and the steam generated is used to drive a turbine.

The Californians were the first to experiment on a large scale with solar concentrating technology, building first Solar One (during the 80's) and then the improved Solar Two (in the mid 90's) near the small town of Daggett, just off the fabled Route 66. Alas, investment for bigger and better plants was elusive and Solar Two was dismantled in 2009. However, these early projects paved the way for Spain to lead the current renaissance in solar power. There are now two solar towers in Andalusia, with the largest, PS20, producing 20MW of power that is fed into the grid to supply energy for Seville. The hope is that by 2013 a range of solar power technologies will provide a total of 300MW for the region. These technologies will include parabolic mirrors focusing solar energy onto an array of tubes rather than on to a central tower.

PS20 is surrounded by over 1000 huge sun-tracking heliostat mirrors that must be kept meticulously clean to run at optimum levels, and the area around the tower becomes so bright that water vapour and dust is illuminated in an otherworldly aura. In 2009 Californians got back into the solar tower game with the opening of the Sierra SunTower, which uses steam power to drive 5MW of clean energy to the grid. These types of plants take up a great deal of countryside but it is claimed that if just a small fraction of the Sahara desert was covered with solar towers then all the electricity needs of Europe could be met.

SOLAR TOWER

Cats like to roll around in paper.

I use paper, lots of it. I hate flat 'computer' colour so I paint the paper with cheap gouache – that way even something simple like a circle becomes more interesting. I work to a large scale by hand so that can I see the whole picture and then I shrink the parts together in Photoshop. My studio is really messy and my cat loves to crawl around in all the paper. I would love to be more tidy but I work so quickly that everything goes everywhere. Because I prefer working on the computer I guess I rush through the first part. I love secondhand shopping for old stuff like retro printed textiles; I seem to have some kind of nostalgia for the past but I'm not sure why. I take lots of photos and often get inspired by images that I see in the newspaper or on the TV.

Swedish kings and incarcerated artists.

I'm really interested in history and crafts. I admire the work of Sven Erixon, a painter who worked in strong colours in the naive style during the 1930's, and I've recently become fascinated with the artist Esther Henning, who lived in a mental institution for most of her life. There was a documentary about her on Swedish TV this year and I love the way she drew with embroidery, using it like paint. I was given a very open brief to depict companionship for the design of a menu for the Riche restaurant in Stockholm and I kept thinking about this song from my childhood about being nice to people and sharing an apple or playing football, so the scene is intentionally very naive and reminds me of my kindergarten in the woods. I included a great big grey tower block to take an edge off the cuteness and because I've always been fascinated by them. Vasaloppet was made as part of a book about the Swedish king Gustav Vasa and in this picture he is escaping from the Danes. We have a tradition of holding an annual race in his honour every winter. I love the way that such bizarre historical details are remembered.

Andalusian foxes and slicked-back hair.

People complain about renewable technologies being unattractive but what struck me about the solar tower in Seville is just how beautiful it is, with the sunlight rotating in beams around this building that looks like something out of a science fiction movie. I started my research on the internet, where I was inspired by the hot colours of Spain to give the characters a lazy holiday feel from another era. For the central man I used a screen shot that I took of this guy on a TV show about art in the 80's: I loved the look of his classic 80's glasses and slicked-back hair. At the front a little girl is holding her glasses up to the sun, which heats the water and makes a little paper windmill spin around. I included traditional architecture and Andalusian foxes and deer because they are very common in this part of Spain. The idea that humans and animals can co-exist in a better way is an aspiration for the future and there are three solar towers because it would be great if we could build lots of them. I'm quite stubborn, so even if I'm getting really angry with a design I won't stop working on it: I did four different versions of the solar tower until I was happy. It helps to have a few things on the go at the same time so that I can stand back from a project until I see it more clearly.

It's a difficult life, my friends.

I am not currently making a living as an illustrator because I've been so busy since graduating from the London College of Communication and moving to Bordeaux in south west France where I now live with my boyfriend. (well that's my excuse anyway – I've been kept quite busy learning French). Being an illustrator is tough, so having your own website and promotional material to mail out is a must. Art school was great because I made lots of friends and we were able to help each other out, something that I miss now that I'm so far away. I didn't realise how lonely being an illustrator could be; it just wasn't something I considered before I started my course. Most of the time I have to make decisions by myself or with my boyfriend but ideally I would like to work with other people with whom I click artistically. I enjoy entering work for design briefs because challenge makes my work more interesting. Eventually I'd love to illustrate for children's books and there is a good scene for that in France; I like the idea that someone else writes the words that I have to find a way to illustrate in an effective way.

Vasaloppet

CRAIG YAMEY

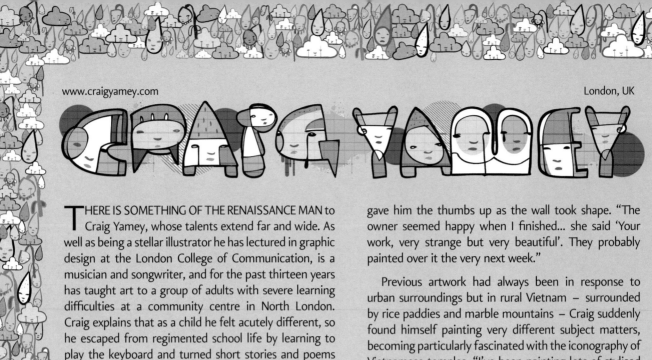

THERE IS SOMETHING OF THE RENAISSANCE MAN to Craig Yamey, whose talents extend far and wide. As well as being a stellar illustrator he has lectured in graphic design at the London College of Communication, is a musician and songwriter, and for the past thirteen years has taught art to a group of adults with severe learning difficulties at a community centre in North London. Craig explains that as a child he felt acutely different, so he escaped from regimented school life by learning to play the keyboard and turned short stories and poems into song lyrics. Meanwhile his painting skills flourished under the guidance of a brilliant GCSE art teacher.

Craig has enjoyed a far from set career path. A degree in Graphic Design from the University of Brighton was followed by "a year of freelancing... and pfaffing about!" He struggled to discover where he fit in, eventually returning to study for an MA at Central Saint Martins in Communication Design, which lead to a stable job at a graphics company designing stickers and badges for charities. It was a paradoxical situation in which Craig felt stifled by the lack of creativity in a supposedly creative job. He knew he needed a break. "I decided to get as far away from a computer as I could. I needed to look for fresh stimulation in other places."

Craig rediscovered his mojo during a nine month expedition around the world, sketchbook firmly in hand. He found himself drawing at every opportunity; on buses, in his hotel room and in restaurants. All this in a computer-free zone. "It was great to get my hands dirty again and my head was soon racing with ideas for my return." In Vietnam he memorably offered to paint the walls of a coffee shop in return for a constant flow of iced coffees and avocado shakes. "When the owner saw my drawings she looked at me with a mixture of gratitude and fear. I guess Half Woman Half Bird Crying Tears is a bit much first thing in the morning." All the cool teens

gave him the thumbs up as the wall took shape. "The owner seemed happy when I finished... she said 'Your work, very strange but very beautiful'. They probably painted over it the very next week."

Previous artwork had always been in response to urban surroundings but in rural Vietnam – surrounded by rice paddies and marble mountains – Craig suddenly found himself painting very different subject matters, becoming particularly fascinated with the iconography of Vietnamese temples. "I've been painting lots of stylised faces with a slight Eastern influence and references to the four elements that feature so heavily in Vietnamese art." Crying ladies and men with heads of fire transcend gender and ethnicity, "almost as if to show a sense of 'oneness' between people regardless of their origins." In Hoi An he visited an old calligraphy master to learn traditional techniques and since then his new favourite tool has been Chinese ink. "It's given my work an entirely new aesthetic."

Now Craig is back home putting his new medium into effect. "When I was travelling I limited myself to painting fairly small but since I've been back I've been painting on a much larger scale, up to A1." He keeps separate work spaces so that he doesn't get in too much of a mess. "One area is for getting my hands dirty, and the other is where the computer lives." He paints figures and shapes then brings them into Photoshop to fiddle around with textures and layers. Craig places great importance on the process of creating an image. "A lot of my work is based purely on aesthetics so I don't feel driven to post-rationalise my work. Although people often find meaning in my art that I didn't intend and that's okay too."

The self sufficiency of those outside the grip of Western consumerism was an eye-opener. "I've tried to

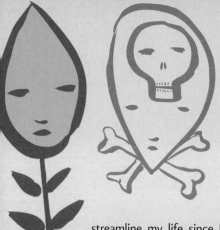

streamline my life since I've come home." Like many, he gets frustrated with the counterproductive environmental schemes that London councils implement. "East Finchley's designated spot for recycling is so far away that nearly everyone drives there!" His depiction of alternative energy shows rotary kites high up in the atmosphere between sky and space. Slipstream currents convert wind power into electrical energy, in an animate world where everything has a face "to show that they're alive with energy."

Music remains Craig's main passion. "I get the biggest high from performing live." He then ponders this statement. "But I shouldn't say that in this interview should I?" It's definitely very honest, and leads to a discussion of the way that music can scratch an itch that illustration can't quite reach. "Illustration is very isolated," he explains, "the interaction with other musicians is something that I love. A lot of illustrators will say that weeks can pass and they haven't seen a single soul because they're meeting deadlines." He doesn't mind the solitary nature of an illustrator's working life until he's been alone awhile. "I'm not a gregarious party animal but at the same time I get to a point where I need to chat to people. If I've been working alone for two weeks I'll get on the tube and start talking to strangers!" As for the future of his new-found illustration techniques? "I want to see my work on murals, crockery and t-shirts. I've got the ideas, now I just need a bit more commercial activity."

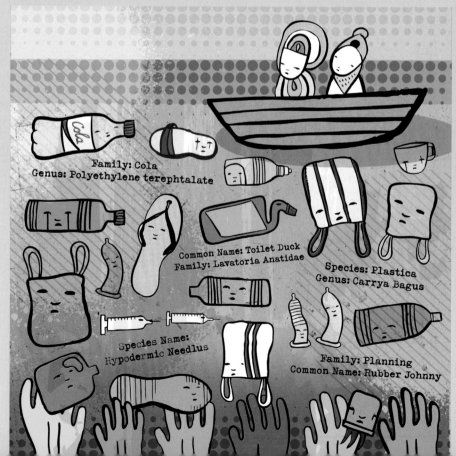

Family: Cola
Genus: Polyethylene terephtalate

Common Name: Toilet Duck
Family: Lavatoria Anatidae

Species: Plastica
Genus: Carrya Bagus

Species Name:
Hypodermic Needlus

Family: Planning
Common Name: Rubber Johnny

AUSTRALIAN PROFESSOR Bryan Roberts has been looking for many decades for ways to harness high altitude wind power, and has come up with an invention that crosses a helicopter with a kite to create a flying wind turbine, known as a Flying Electric Generator or FEG. A few years ago his invention was discovered by Californian based David Shepard, (an engineer who made his name cracking codes during the Second World War) and together they took out a US patent in 2007 shortly before David died and his son PJ Shepard took over.

Their company, Sky WindPower, retains plans to send these tethered 'kiteplanes' 10km up into the jet stream – where the strongest, steadiest and most persistent winds occur, up to hundred times stronger than close to earth. Made from lightweight carbon fibre and steel alloy, the kiteplanes fly skywards using motors to drive the propeller blades like a helicopter before stabilising in the stratosphere. Here, wind pulses across the propeller blades and holds the whole whirligig contraption aloft as dynamos generate energy which is sent back down to a base station via aluminium cables. Should there be a lull in the wind the dynamos can again switch into motors to keep the generator airborne.

On each kiteplane four rotors sweep a diameter of 11m to produce 10MW, enough electricity to power ten thousand homes. Sounds implausible? Bryan has already proven that the basic principle can work but there are various issues to be resolved, like how to retain the generator's position as the jet stream meanders across the sky without the cables getting tangled. There is also the issue of passing aircraft that could possibly get caught up in the tethers. Sky WindPower point out that there are balloons carrying radar equipment to detect illegal flights tethered at altitudes of up to 5km at various sites along the southern borders of the US and these are

shown on the aeronautical charts used by pilots. Kiteplane farms situated in remote locations could supply the whole of the US whilst taking up less than one four hundredth of the air space and could thus be easily avoided. Another major problem could be the cables acting as huge lightening conductors, and it has been suggested that the energy could be beamed back to earth instead. If a particularly savage electrical storm struck, the current plan involves landing the machines but this is clearly impractical for continuous energy production.

TIME Magazine voted Sky WindPower's Flying Electric Generator one of the best inventions of 2008, so despite the need for massive amounts of further testing it can be seen that the idea is a tantalising one. As the esteemed climate scientist Ken Caldeira points out, harvesting just 1% of high altitude winds could produce enough energy for the whole world.

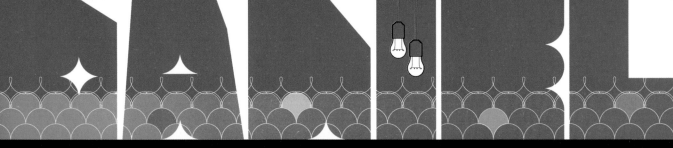

DANIEL ROSSI completed a degree in industrial design and visual communication in Canada, but now works from his own space in the Little Mountain studios in Eindhoven, Holland. "My parents are both Italian so I always dreamed of moving to Europe. I would have gone to northern Italy, but my girlfriend is half Dutch so I came here to be with her." Many of his friends left home in Alberta to find work in Montreal and Vancouver. "The graphic design opportunities in my hometown are all corporate, so experimental work is not exactly appreciated and I always felt like a bit of a renegade." In the Netherlands Daniel is able to experiment to his heart's delight, crossing between different disciplines, and mixing up product design and graphic design to create fantastical objects. "I hate restrictions and I like blurring boundaries, so I tend to draw things and then bring them to life in three dimensions, experimenting as I go."

Was moving country hard? "When I got here it was a huge shock but I adapted quickly when the survival instinct kicked in; networking and submitting my work to everyone in the hope of a job." Daniel's first Dutch commission was to create a logo for a local government housing organisation. "I was lucky because they really helped me to establish myself here with all the right contacts." Is he making a living from his art now? "I'm getting by – so far," he says modestly.

Daniel has a maverick attitude to his working practice. "I'm quite chaotic, so my desk is covered in cardboard and paper. I've tried to work in sketchbooks but I'm not very good at structure." He works with whatever materials present themselves and is equally at home painting on a wall or sketching in Illustrator. "It's my right arm!" he quips. "I'm really messy in Illustrator too – you should see one of my artboards."

Daniel cites a variety of influences on his work, including Alexander Girard – a prominent textile designer during the 1950's, comic artist Jamie Hewlett, product designer Jaime Hayon, Alphonse Mucha and Spanish architect Gaudi. "Even though some people think his buildings are over the top I think they're genius." He's also into graphic novels. "Whatever I'm reading at a particular time tends to influence my style. It's forever changing and evolving but I like that because I get bored quite quickly."

Has he ever worried about reactions to his art? "I used to be fearful of negative comments but now I just wait for the dust to settle after finishing a piece [before I ask for opinions] so that I can revisit the work with a fresh mind." Advice is good for him. "I've learnt to appreciate other people's opinions and different perspectives. Sometimes they push me in directions that I would never have thought of alone." As a result he shows his work to "pretty much anyone. Sometimes I even show my mum."

"I never considered myself to be actively involved in the environmental movement before I started working on this brief," confesses Daniel. Did he have trouble getting his head around the idea of illustrating renewable energy? "To begin with, yes," Daniel admits. "My first thought was 'oh god, I'll have to be too scientific and structured' but then I got excited about exploring technological solutions in a fantastical rather than analytical way." Daniel's chosen method of renewable energy hasn't hit the mainstream yet, but he's thrilled by its potential. "Because it's flexible Power Plastic could be used on many different surfaces and buildings and I found it fascinating to explore the concept of this new world," he says. "I wanted to bring out an attractive, playful aspect." Daniel decided to wrap Power Plastic around buildings. "Imagine a city as one large circuit board. The buildings and monuments create their own power, so the street lamps and traffic lights can literally be plugged into them." This brief has been an eye-opener. "If we're going to save the environment let's at least make it look nice in the process! There are so many exciting possibilities for the application of art and design to help technology and the environment."

Two of Hearts for Amelia's Magazine Shelter Card Quilt

INVENTION, as Thomas Edison remarked, is 1% inspiration and 99% perspiration. The idea for the modern steam engine came to James Watt in a flash as he was strolling across Glasgow Green one Sunday, but it took him ten years of experiment to get it right. So no one expects new technologies to take off comprehensively without a few teething issues.

The first generation of solar cells use silicon and have been around for some time – they represent the great majority of photovoltaic cells in use today despite the high production costs of growing silicon crystals slowly at high temperatures. The second generation use thin films of exotic materials (cadmium, indium, tellurium et al) and hold out the promise of lower production costs, which have yet to occur. The third generation of solar cells is made from thin films of organic molecules.

Dr. Alan Heeger, winner of the Nobel Prize for chemistry in 2000, co-founded Konarka in Massachusetts in 2001 to develop his third generation cell. Almost accidentally, Heeger had discovered that by combining a spherical carbon molecule (a fullerene: discovered itself as recently as 1985) with a plastic polymer, the polymer becomes photo-reactive. Konarka's photovoltaic gloop can be printed like an ink onto long rolls of plastic to create large areas of cheap and flexible solar cells. Power Plastic, as it is called, can be used in a myriad of applications: in anything that is made of plastic and anywhere that power is needed. Heeger believes that his invention could reduce the cost of solar power by a factor as high as twenty and all materials used are fully recyclable.

But there are problems. Power Plastic is a mere 5% efficient compared with the 15-20% efficiency of traditional silicon solar cells, and Konarka is currently concentrating on projects such as portable, electricity-generating buildings for the military, wearable textile electronics, sun-bags that can be used to charge mobile phones and even advertising panels on soft drinks bottles – hardly the kind of focus that is needed to reverse global warming and provide third world energy solutions. The latest news suggests that the company may be collaborating on the construction of shade structures in North Africa and the Middle East but just imagine what other fantastic solutions they could come up with if they succeed in providing affordable coverings for any kind of building or structure, everywhere in the world.

power plastic

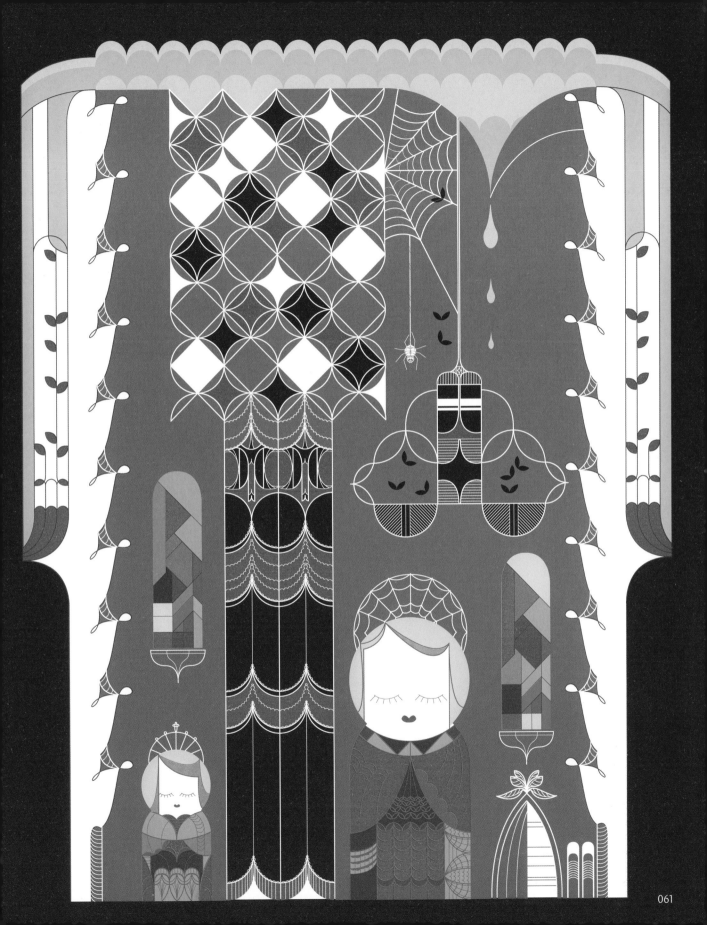

THE EARLIEST TIDAL POWER came in the form of tidal mills. Excavations show that there was one situated on the River Fleet in central London (long paved over) during Roman times. By the 1700's there were over 70 tidal mills in London and the largest surviving tidal mill in the world remains at Three Mills on the River Lea in the East End.

Tidal mills have always been on a small scale. A bolder idea is to construct a barrage across an entire estuary, such as the one across the River Rance in France. Completed in the 1960's, it consists of 24 turbines that produce power sufficient for around 140,000 homes at a cheaper cost than the next cheapest source in France: nuclear. In the UK a similar barrage across the Severn Estuary has been hotly debated for over a century. Many feel that the environmental impacts of such a huge structure would cause insurmountable problems, so it has never left the drawing board.

The problems of a barrage can be avoided by using 'in stream' turbines, which directly tap the energy of a tidal current without disrupting ecosystems. Hence the name EnCurrent for the turbines being developed by a Canadian company, New Energy Corporation of Alberta. Using floating pontoons the units can easily and cheaply be towed into place wherever they are needed and can be deployed singly, in series or in parallel along man-made canals and rivers. The generators are kept above the waterline so that they can easily be accessed and because the blades rotate slowly in an open design there is room for fish to swim through. One commercial test project in Manitoba was successfully connected to the grid in 2008, and the company is gradually scaling up the size of the turbines. Why dam a river when you can keep it free-flowing?

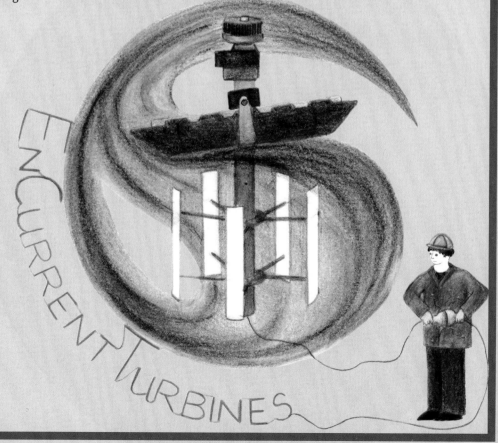

EnCurrent Turbines

When Emma Raby is not creating her delicate and whimsical illustrations you might find her taking a long walk. (Notable achievement: navigating the coast to coast route across Northern England, from St Bees to Robin Hoods Bay). She also prides herself on baking a mean raspberry cheesecake in the blink of an eye and being a "reasonably good" ice-skater, but all of these are currently taking a back seat to drawing.

When did you start drawing?

As a child I was fascinated with spiders so I made lots of felt tip drawings of them and put together little sticky tape books. I also spent a lot of time copying illustrations from Beano and books such as Alice in Wonderland. When I started my art and design foundation I had hoped to go on to study graphic design but my tutor told me that I wouldn't like it because there wasn't enough drawing, so I decided to do Illustration at the University of Plymouth, which was great. The course put a big emphasis on working with other students and learning from each other so it seems very lonely now that I've left. I have two goldfish called Linus and Lucy (after the characters in Charles Schulz's cartoons). Lucy is very bossy and chases Linus around the tank... but they don't really replace a room full of illustrators!

So where and how do you work now?

I have two very big desks in front of the window in my bedroom, and they take up a lot of space. I keep an awful lot of books around my desk but the one I would save first in a fire is British Folktales and Legends by Katherine Briggs. I also have close at hand Ronald and the Wizard Calico by Emanuelle Luzzati, an illustrated novel called The Three Incestuous Sisters by Audrey Niffenegger, Pupshaw & Pushpaw, a surrealist picture book by Jim Woodring and a graphic novel by David B. I like my desks to be quite cluttered with all my materials and the things that are inspiring me for the project I'm working on. I listen to audio books or Radio 4, especially comedy such as The Hitchhikers Guide to the Galaxy, Bleak Expectations and Old Harry's Game. I often use a mix of different media, particularly for coloured work, but my preferred tools to work with are pencil, graphite and an eraser. My work involves very little computer design, I mostly use it for cleaning up images and for working with colour separations.

Are there certain themes that crop up in your work?

The main theme that I seem to return to is looking through windows or water. Although I'm not really sure why that is. I'm also told that I seem to like boring suburban housing. I think I am very affected by my surroundings, and my work tends to change depending on where I am, so when I was in Plymouth I got really into the landscape there and often tried to fit the sea or Dartmoor into my illustrations. Now that I am back at home with my parents in Kettering, Northamptonshire I've been going out on long walks so that I can get back into drawing trees. I think the dark element of my work comes from an interest in ruined abbeys and medieval art.

What are you working on at the moment?

My course at university was very close-knit so we plan to continue working together as a group called Marmalade Beard. We all work in very different ways, so the output of the group is quite diverse. Most of the work I am doing at the moment is for my portfolio; I'm applying to do the Children's Book Illustration MA at Anglia Ruskin University. I'm working on a folk tale from Northamptonshire called The Farmer and The Boggart and I am trying to find more stories from around where I live. The Dead Moon is a story that was collected by Katherine Briggs – it tells of the moon visiting the earth, only to be trapped in the fens until she is released by men from a local village when they realise the moon is missing from the sky. In five years time I would really like to be writing children's books.

What did you learn from this brief?

I was already aware of renewable technologies that are in more widespread use but I was surprised to find out how many are being tested on a smaller scale. I liked the idea of the EnCurrent Turbine because it is such a low impact grassroots technology: it catches the current in rivers and each unit can power up to twelve houses. I find books to be friendlier than the internet for researching, so I discovered Compton's Improved Wave Power and Tidal Motor in a book called Edwardian Inventions by Rodney Dale and Joan Gray. A boat is fixed to a tower and pivots in the rocking motion of the sea, which drives a shaft fixed to a series of cogs, which are connected to a generator. In the illustration I showed how this design would have worked, and also the Edwardian habit of taking tea in some very strange places. It was patented in 1904 and yet after all this time, energy from the waves is still not realising its full potential.

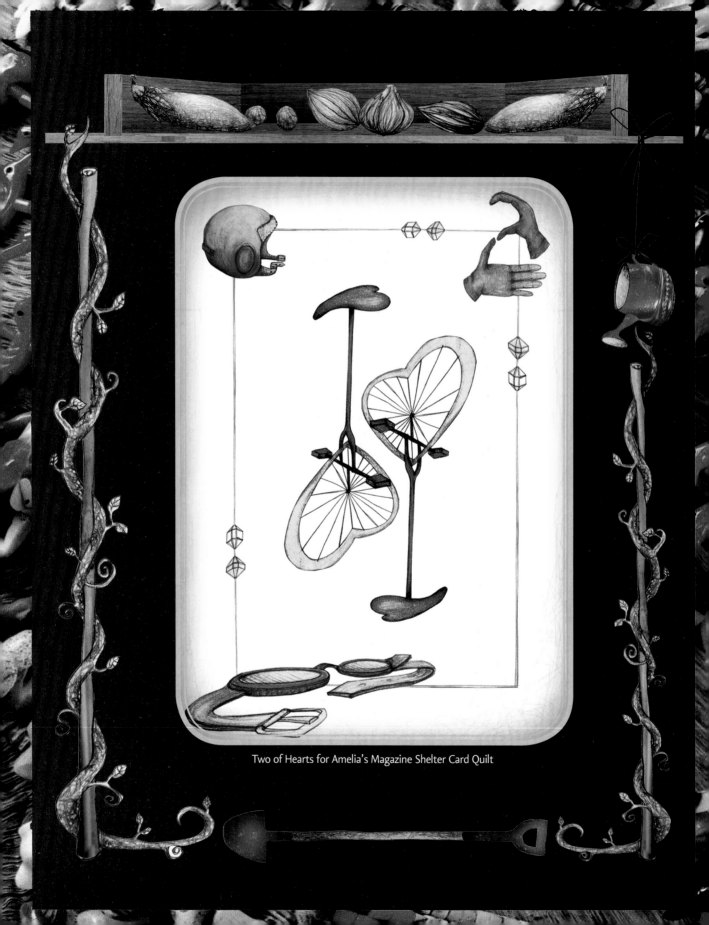

Two of Hearts for Amelia's Magazine Shelter Card Quilt

Wave dragon

WALES is synonymous with the red dragon that appears on the national flag. It therefore seems hugely appropriate that a new wave energy converter called the Wave Dragon is being pioneered three miles off the coast of Pembrokeshire near Milford Haven. And surely it is no coincidence that the Wave Dragon is painted red.

Well actually, it is. The Wave Dragon was invented by a Dane called Erik Friis-Madsen, who was inspired whilst standing on a beach in 1986 watching waves overtop the reef of a South Pacific atoll. The initial Wave Dragon sketch shows a circular structure, a floating atoll, with a turbine in the centre. Interestingly, the final prototype was named because of its similarity to the shape of a kite: in Danish the same word is used for both kite and dragon.

Since 1997 Erik has been putting those first beach brainwaves into practice and by 2003 a scale model in an inlet at Nissum Bredning in Denmark began to supply power to the grid. The full-scale Welsh version of the Wave Dragon will be the biggest wave generator in the world, producing 7MW at peak capacity. It will be built at Pembroke Dock and tested a few miles offshore where it will be well out of the way of shipping lanes, before being deployed to the high seas twelve miles off the coast alongside a whole family of sea-guzzling Wave Dragons. This pioneer unit should offer ample opportunity for visits from nosy visitors.

In the meantime this opportunity for visits

But how does this Wave Dragon beast work? Well, the name is a bit of a clue: It is essentially a floating barge with very large (red) jaws facing the oncoming waves. The jaws eat the waves by scooping up the tops and channelling the water into a large tank which then drains out through some turbines to produce electricity. That's it. It uses foolproof technology that has been used for nearly a century in the hydropower industry and it is claimed that in a high energy wave climate, i.e. somewhere pretty darn stormy, one Wave Dragon could produce 50GW hours per year. That's a lot of energy. And did we mention how big the Wave Dragon is? The jaws are a massive 300m wide; that's more than twice the size of a football pitch! A monster indeed.

www.emmiojala.eu   Alkmaar, Netherlands

I've always been fascinated by new inventions – how they work and what they would look like – and I'm a bit of an idealist, so illustrating a more sustainable world was a lot of fun. I found some of the names for the alternative technologies intriguing and the Wave Dragon really triggered my imagination. The concept sounds so fantastical yet it actually exists! To start with I read up on it from the internet and watched films of the trial off the coast in Wales. I thought the name sounded incredibly alive, but the idea of a huge machine in the middle of the sea can be a bit frightening so I decided to give the dragon a friendly personality.

The Wave Dragon eats waves to make energy and it is such a simple idea that I can't help but wonder why dragons weren't invented at the same time as windmills. The Wave Dragon is huge and powerful yet mysterious. However, its purpose in life is very important and it does only good for the world. By making the enormous machine approachable rather than soulless I hope to highlight the good intention behind the technology. It's exciting to have the opportunity to visualise a tangible solution for a better, sustainable future.

I'm completely self-taught. When I was a child I filled my room with homemade spaceships and paper crocodiles, then as I became older I spent hours drawing with charcoals from our fireplace. Now I love to tinker around on Photoshop and Illustrator to create imaginary realities from objects I have made and drawn, photographs and found materials. I like computers because they make experimenting so easy but I want to keep an authentic hand drawn feel. Pencils rock as much as Photoshop.

My style exists because of the materials I use so I definitely work best at home with all of them around me. I use brown wrapping paper, masking tape, leftover fabrics, buttons and teabag wrappers, which come in such cool colours. I like to draw on unconventional things such as newspapers and I make old books into sketchbooks. It's fun to experiment with materials, so I don't throw things in the bin straight away – perhaps the orange peel I left on the table last night could be of some, as yet unknown, use.

I'm from Jyväskylä in Finland although I now study at the Amsterdam Fashion Institute in the Netherlands. Even though I have never formally studied illustration my teachers and fellow students encourage me to include it within my work, and their support and encouragement makes me think I can be more than just a doodler. I'm sure my upbringing has influenced my aesthetic because I tend to use natural tones, I find simple compositions easiest to work with and I often have urges to include space in my work, all of which are typical to Scandinavian style.

There are many talented illustrators who inspire me to draw, and their work is but a simple click away on the internet. I cannot highlight enough how blogs are such a good source of inspiration – they're just a great way to showcase work and the online illustration scene has a really nice vibe. I love the way that children view the world and all its possibilities in a rather naive way, so I strive to see this way myself. I take notice of lots of small ordinary phenomena that others might miss and incorporate these stories into my work. I was once out walking when I chanced upon a glove lying on the ground at the traffic lights with a cigarette still smoking in the palm as if still held in a hand. It felt as if the glove was so alive yet somehow full of melancholy and I immediately found myself wondering about the story behind it.

There are big differences in temperature between the seasons in Finland, so it is incredibly easy to notice unusual temperature changes. Consequently the Finns are very conscious of climate change and worried about the fact that it now rains more than it snows during the winter and many species are spreading north into new areas that were previously uninhabitable but are now warming up. In Amsterdam the Beyond Green symposium tackles sustainability in the Dutch fashion industry and the fashion academy makes sure there are frequent lectures on the subject. I'm very concerned about climate change and actively trying to reduce my carbon footprint – I hope that choosing a paper bag over a plastic one or walking instead of taking a car will help at least a little and being aware of the environment influences my work even at the level of execution: I try to use what I find around me rather than having to purchase new materials.

Our society could be so much better if only people would realise that there is no point in being so egotistical. The attitude "I'm going to do it because I can" doesn't get us anywhere because someone has to pay the price in the end. To create a better future both environmentally and socially we have to think beyond what is in it for ourselves and consider the effect that our actions will have on the world around us.

French aeronautical engineer Georges Darrieus came up with the famous 'egg-whisk' design for vertical axis wind turbines in the late 1920's. Acolytes of his design claim it is superior because it can handle wind from any direction and so, for example is better suited to urban environments. However, traditional horizontal axis turbines can be built far larger. This is because the straight blades of the Darrieus design start to suffer destructive vibrations as they get bigger, eventually snapping in two.

Hydroelectric power is currently dominated by expensive dams which cause massive environmental problems, and it was Alexander Gorlov's experience in helping to construct the Aswan Dam in Egypt that convinced him that there had to be a better way to produce power from water. An activist who fled Russia during the 1970's, he was hired by Northeastern University in Boston, where he became determined to improve on the original Darrieus turbine for underwater use, having found that it worked better than any other design despite vibration problems. So he twisted the vertical turbine blades into a helical shape (like a strand of DNA) thereby smoothing the vibration and improving efficiency. The Gorlov Helical Turbine was patented in 1994 as a way of providing sustainable 'free-flow' hydroelectric power.

When placed into a current the Gorlov Helical Turbine will kick into motion almost instantly and tests have shown that it can capture 35% of kinetic energy, an improvement on the 20% captured by a conventional turbine. Unlike other turbines, Gorlov's device works well regardless of the direction of water flow, so it can be mounted either horizontally or vertically, stacked in rows like spools on a string, and placed in water as shallow as 1m.

A few queries remain unanswered concerning the effect of debris in the turbines and problems for water wildlife. Gorlov claims that a pressure barrier around each machine effectively keeps fish away, but whilst this may be true for a single device it could be a very different scenario when aquatic animals encounter a whole row of whirling turbines. Nonetheless GCK Technology is mass producing easy-to-put-together turbines that can easily be installed in remote locations, including one already operating successfully in the Amazon in Brazil.

But Gorlov dreams of bigger things: an array of helical turbines under the Golden Gate Bridge that would power the whole of San Francisco. And more ambitious still, a huge farm of helical turbines that harness the immense energy of the Gulf Stream to supply enough energy for the entire US. What taking a significant amount of kinetic energy from such a crucial ocean current might do to the climates that rely on its warming currents, is not something that has been discussed too widely.

Such visions may seem like madness, but a large scale deployment of the Gorlov Helical Turbine is already underway. In 1999, an article in the Financial Times caught the interest of South Korea's National Assembly, who invited Gorlov to deliver a presentation on his invention. Korea just so happens to be surrounded by fast-moving water and the Koreans began a major test of Gorlov's turbine in 2002 in the Uldolmok Strait, a tidal channel between the Korean Peninsula and Jindo Island. A permanent turbine array intended to generate 100MW will be installed soon.

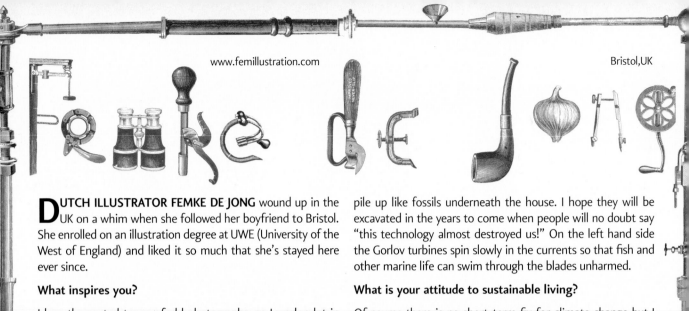

Femke de Jong

DUTCH ILLUSTRATOR FEMKE DE JONG wound up in the UK on a whim when she followed her boyfriend to Bristol. She enrolled on an illustration degree at UWE (University of the West of England) and liked it so much that she's stayed here ever since.

What inspires you?

I love the muted tones of old photographs, so I work a lot in sepia and 'off colours'. I used to take a lot of mechanical objects apart when I was a kid so that I could make up new inventions from the separate bits. Once pulled apart the cogs have a kind of romantic quality to them; a bit weird and almost sinister. Nowadays I go to lots of car-boot sales and flea markets to collect mechanical parts, and I take pictures of the plumbing... I've had some quizzical looks when I've been caught taking pictures in the pub toilet. I construct little machines by layering montages out of all the old stuff I collect – sometimes it's hard to get the mechanical element into editorial briefs but I usually manage to include it somewhere.

Can you describe the process of montage?

When I find cool things I scan them into my computer and organise them into folders with sub sections so that I can easily pull them out for inspiration and to put them together in Photoshop. I have a brainstorm then I do a lot of sketching so if I go off on random tangents I can use my roughs as a guide back. When I'm collaging in Photoshop the mood can change abruptly if I put in something unexpected, so I try to stick with the initial plan even though there is less likelihood of happy accidents. I find working on a computers useful when there is a tight deadline to meet, but I often feel like throwing mine out of the window! I tried doing animation but found it too frustrating to spend so much time in front of the computer.

What's happening in your main image?

I've been wanting to create an image about sustainable technology for some time now so this seemed such an appropriate brief. We crave new technologies all the time and yet as soon as they are no longer of use we disregard them: on the right side old mechanical parts pile up like fossils underneath the house. I hope they will be excavated in the years to come when people will no doubt say "this technology almost destroyed us!" On the left hand side the Gorlov turbines spin slowly in the currents so that fish and other marine life can swim through the blades unharmed.

What is your attitude to sustainable living?

Of course there is no short-term fix for climate change but I believe that small things can help. Working on this brief has actually made me want a garden even more! We need to start considering the life span of material things; when old-fashioned everyday objects are still fine to use, why do we always buy new ones which usually only last for a fraction of the time? (And are designed that way so that manufacturers can sell more stuff). We should re-use, re-make and re-appropriate in real life, and also in illustration and design and art. Because illustration can be playful it doesn't have to be preachy and as a result people are more likely to get the message. I'm passionate about illustration because it's such a powerful tool for bringing opinions into the world.

Do you work with other people?

With my friends in Hot Soup I've collaborated on set designs for parties and now I'd like to get another studio in a collective space so I can stay in touch with other people's opinions. It's fun to work with other people but at the other end of the spectrum I also need my own space and

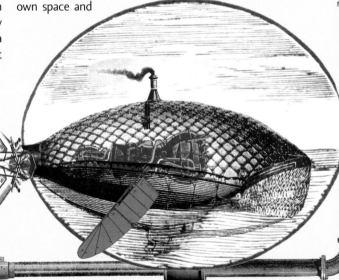

sometimes I end up working through the night alone. Being self-critical is very important to me otherwise I won't push myself and my work will be shit. I'm my own biggest critic! But it's always good to have another pair of eyes to look over things and say what's not quite right – my boyfriend Mark is good for the odd bit of criticism even though he isn't an illustrator. I guess that's why collective studios are good; as places to get quick and direct feedback from others.

Where does music fit into your life?

I like listening to music that can be slightly in the background when I'm working, so nothing with full-on beats: nostalgic music and jazz. I used to make music and feel I've adopted a really good working ethic from that – I guess my illustration is multi-layered like music often is, and it's hard to appreciate the whole until all the layers are in place. I've done illustrations for album covers, which I really enjoy when I like the music. It becomes a really personal piece, like a musical collage. I would get more involved with the music culture in the UK but I don't want to get into the drinking side of things.

So where next?

It takes a couple of years for an illustrator to get established after university, so I'm aware I'll probably have to keep a little day job on the side until I am established and have got all the right contacts. On the side I give private tuition in Photoshop, but more and more illustration briefs are coming in, so I need to be ready for them if I want one day to make a full time living from illustration .

KITE GEN

Inventors all over the world struggled for years to design a working aeroplane but it was the Wright Brothers who cracked it. Their secret was the realisation that what mattered was how the plane was controlled. A hundred years later, inventors are trying to perfect the flight of huge high altitude kites to generate electricity. But anyone who has flown a kite on a blustery day knows that this might not be so simple. Which brings us back to the Wright brothers. The problem is control. The kite needs to be kept aloft and then brought back in with extreme precision.

Kite Gen was founded in 2007 by two Italians, Massimo Ippolito, kite surfer and sailing enthusiast, and Mario Milanese, a professor at the Polytechnic of Turin. Their invention involves flying lightweight kites up into the atmosphere via two light wires a mere 3mm in diameter and 800m long. Once they have reached maximum height these intelligent kites fold down to a position of least resistance and can be retrieved by motorised winches using a fraction of the energy that is generated during the unravelling stage. As the cycle is repeated ad infinitum the height and path of the kites can be adjusted in a synchronised dance across the sky.

All the predictions suggest that a Kite Gen farm would be cheap to construct and maintain because the turbines work with the wind's strength rather than against it, and all heavy machinery remains on the ground. On a carousel the spools for twenty automatically controlled kites steer a huge circular track 1,600 metres in diameter at a speed of fifteen revolutions per hour. This can generate 1GW of power, equivalent to a medium size nuclear power station, but estimated to cost ten times less to implement (and offering much cleaner safer energy). All the technology is concentrated along a circular path so the vast majority of the area is available for agricultural activities and because the wires near the ground move very little they are unlikely to cause problems for birds.

In addition Kite Gen propose the deployment of 'stems' – single kite power stations that could be grouped together into farms, or built on their own. They have also considered the possibility of offshore floating generators that could be moored in optimum locations and would be many times lighter than traditional wind turbines.

In 2006 Kite Gen successfully tested a prototype kite up to an altitude of 800m and their first full-scale 3MW generator is now being installed near Asti in Italy. But this is a mere baby compared to their future vision of a mega carousel 25 km in diameter – sort of like a never-ending railway bridge to nowhere – on which rotates a gigantic magnetically levitated Kite Gen. The tethered kites fly upwards 10km in controlled formation, generating more than 60GW...

So, all the bits of hardware seem straightforward, but what about the software? The jury is out on who will be the Wright brothers of high altitude kite power, but at least one person is working on the core problem of precision control: Allister Furey at the University of Sussex, UK is developing a brain-simulating neural network for controlling kites. Wow.

Amelia's Magazine, Earth Listings

Two of Hearts for Amelia's Magazine Shelter Card Quilt

hannah

HANNAH LEWIS likes the artist Kandinsky for his bold graphics, Japanese illustrator Yoshitomo Nara for the way he blends colours and Nate Williams for his use of composition and text. And she's not afraid to big up the work of her old tutor from Southampton Solent University, Jonny Hannah. She currently works for a music licensing company and crams illustration projects into the evenings and weekends.

WHAT ELSE DO YOU LIKE TO DRAW?

I draw a lot of birds because they have such interesting forms; my favourites are seagulls; I like their webbed feet and scavenging nature. They aren't at all elegant but I like their personality – a bit rude! They seemed to be everywhere in California so I became obsessed with taking pictures of them. Now I'm back at home all I see are pigeons.

HOW DO YOU COME UP WITH IDEAS?

I spend a lot of time on the train, so I carry a standard hardback notebook around with me for drawing people. It's a bit embarrassing when they catch me and ask to see their picture because they tend to be really unflattering; I make sure all wrinkles are included! On my trip to California last year I met lots of colourful characters who have since crept into my work.

HOW DO YOU MAKE AN ILLUSTRATION?

I did a degree in illustration but recently I've got more into graphic design and printing, especially DIY and experimental print techniques. I planned to do the whole kite illustration by printing

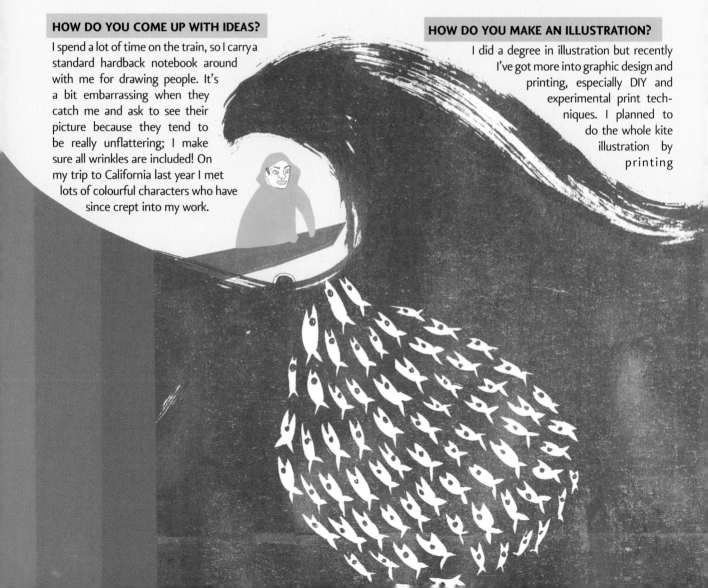

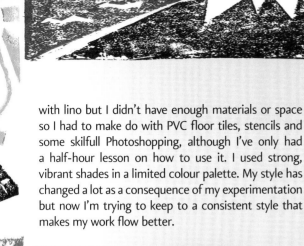

with lino but I didn't have enough materials or space so I had to make do with PVC floor tiles, stencils and some skilfull Photoshopping, although I've only had a half-hour lesson on how to use it. I used strong, vibrant shades in a limited colour palette. My style has changed a lot as a consequence of my experimentation but now I'm trying to keep to a consistent style that makes my work flow better.

HOW DO YOU WORK AND WHERE?

My studio is in my bedroom, which has a big desk in it, but inevitably I spread out around the house and ink gets everywhere. To get in the mood I put Spotify on and listen to everything from Fleet Foxes to Madonna and I mostly work on my own illustrations in the evening, which usually ends up stretching into the early hours. It's all at once or nothing at all. I sit in my room and work for hours. I'm trying to get myself more established by doing competitions and logos for bands, my sister's wedding invitation, that kind of thing. Most people are finding it hard to find work, especially straight out of university; unfortunately I don't have time to devote all my energy to illustration so I'm getting less done than I would like to. I went travelling straight after finishing my degree so when I came back with no money I obviously had to get a job straight-away, although I quite enjoy it and they give me some fun stuff to do – like designing flyers and posters.

WHO HELPS TO CRITIQUE YOUR WORK?

At university I got used to constant feedback so when I left I thought it would be quite hard to motivate myself but I've quickly adapted to the outside world. People at work are all quite creative so they offer criticism and I'm really critical of myself anyway.

HAS THIS BRIEF MADE YOU MORE AWARE?

I think everybody is fairly switched on to environmental issues now, but the brief has definitely made me think. I use water-based eco-friendly ink for printing (which doesn't need to be cleaned up with white spirits) but it was a new idea for me to produce an illustration with a message behind it as I usually draw things just for people to look at and admire. I chose Kite Gen because I was instantly intrigued by the design and there is a distinct possibility that this technology will succeed. I love the idea that kites whizzing around the sky could become part of our landscape – the installation can be sited in almost any location and the unused space in the centre could become a large arena, which I have hinted at with musical notes.

WHAT DOES THE FUTURE HOLD?

I'd love to illustrate a children's book with a comical or dark narrative but feel that I'm still very much at the bottom of the ladder. I'd also like to do front covers for fiction and on the less glamorous side I wouldn't mind doing textbooks. I was looking at some the other day and the idea quite appeals to me!

HANNAH WARREN is a recent MA graduate of the Royal College of Art and is now working full time as an illustrator. Her favourite tipple is a Whiskey Sour, "puts hairs on your chest", and she lives in Bermondsey, London directly behind the Design Museum.

Why did you choose to illustrate the SeaDog?
The name of the SeaDog pump made me want to find out more. During research I discovered that it uses the sea to generate electricity, which I thought was an excellent idea, and one that we are not as familiar with in the UK as we should be, given that the sea takes up two thirds of the world's surface and we live on an island. In Scandinavia wave power is a far more familiar sight than around our own shores and I think it's a great way to produce energy since it does not require any space on already massively oversubscribed land.

How did you construct your main illustration?
I started by researching the images online and then drawing in pens, pencils and ink in my sketchbook. The first stage was quite organic and involved scanning textures and using a scalpel to cut sharp lines, before composing my illustrations in Photoshop where it's easier to rearrange or reshuffle images and elements. I would describe my style as dreamy, folksy and occasionally surreal. Utopia depicts an imaginary place that I'd like to live, where it's always autumn and the housing is all modernist in style. Anansi is a drawing for a west African folk story where the protagonist meets the figure of Death in the forest and accidentally lures him back to the village. I'm also working on an ongoing project to create a children's book based on the Russian folktale of Teryosha, written by Alexei Tolstoy.

A lonely elderly couple fashion a child out of a piece of wood from the forest, sort of like Pinocchio.

What inspires you and how do you work?
Living right by the River Thames is a constant source of inspiration. I like to sit in cafes drawing people who look slightly strange, until they become paranoid and I have to leave. I tend to emphasis their characteristics in an animal-like way. At the moment I am particularly into a folk musician called Chad Van Gaalen. He's from Canada, which I would love to visit, and he self-records and on his latest album plays pretty much every instrument, plus he's a visual artist as well so double respect! I am currently collaborating with another folk musician on a project called Beware the Crow's Bite, which will fuse illustration, animation and moving image with music and live performance. We plan to visit all the London based colleges to encourage partnerships between illustrators and musicians. Working with creatives outside my own discipline is really productive because they often have insights into my work that I can't see myself and I welcome that constructive criticism. During the illustration process I often show my work to my boyfriend, who is a trained graphic designer working with film and video. He's really good with colour compositions and is always my first critic.

Do you use the internet a lot?
I frequently look at the websites of other illustrators – especially those who are doing well – and I follow quite a few blogs. Blogs are basically online sketchbooks for illustrators to showcase their work, often when it's in its early stages and still feels quite personal. I like to get involved in the discussions to learn about new stuff – it's good to discover

HANNAH WARREN

www.hannahwarren.com

London, UK

your passion if you want to be successful. Collectives are a great way for illustrators to work together and I particularly like the Peepshow blog. Another good source of inspiration is the Next Nature website which often uses illustrations to visualise the way that technology has become totally natural and integral to our lives.

Do you make a living from illustration?

Doing an MA at the RCA is an excellent way to network and meet people to collaborate with in the future. It really allowed me to develop my style and indulge myself for two more years and since I've graduated I've been lucky that all my jobs have been related to illustration. My first job was an animated promo for the Disney Channel which came about by chance when I bumped into an old college friend and it wasn't what I had expected to do at all but I really enjoyed it. I've also been involved in a group show called Babel in Shoreditch at Blackall Studios, for which I did large-scale drawings on the origins of language, the learning of language and how we frequently misunderstand each other. But it takes time to establish yourself and there's a lot of groundwork I still need to do!

Can illustrators help increase awareness about climate change?

Research has shown that people don't like to be told that they're doing wrong, but illustrations have the potential to act on a subliminal level to encourage changes in lifestyle. I think it's possible that if an increasing number of artists concentrated on changing our world view on climate change it would have an effect. In the meantime I try to make a difference in my personal life, so I cycle everywhere and buy ethically sound products.

Utopia

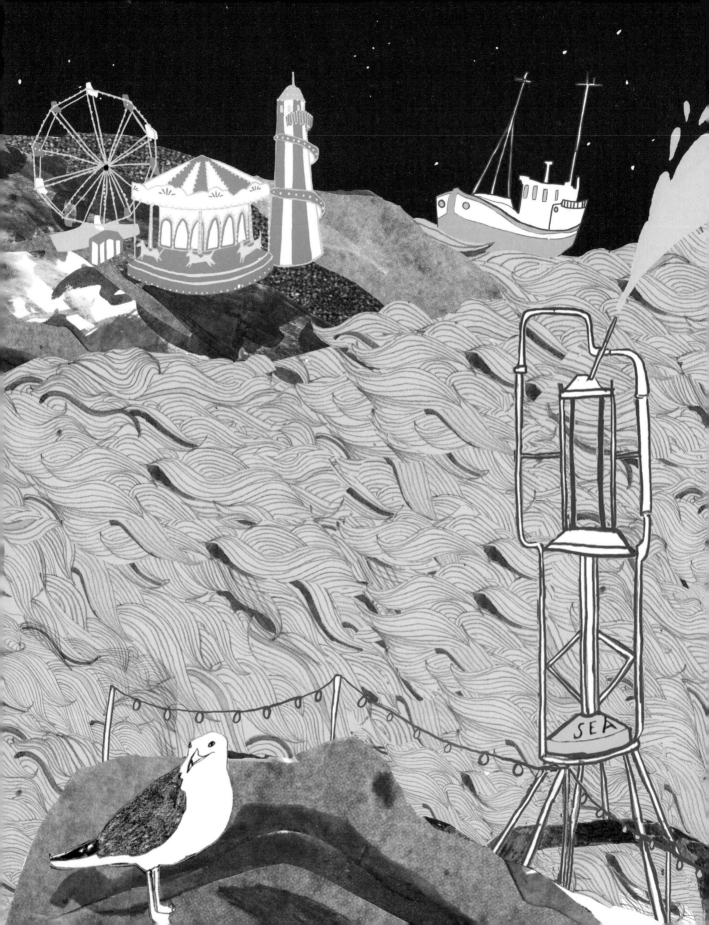

SEA DOG PUMP

AN OLD SEA DOG is a veteran sailor, but there is now a new SeaDog on the block: a simple machine that bobs up and down on the ocean swells and uses a float to drive a piston which pumps seawater to an onshore turbine. Sort of like a large bicycle pump. The SeaDog can be made from readily available materials, contains no electrical or hydraulic components that might suffer damage, can be deployed rapidly and easily scaled up in size, has an open base so that fish can swim through unharmed and can also be used to drive water to shore for de-salinisation purposes. In SeaDog farms the separate units can be easily removed for maintenance without disrupting the entire system.

A team of enthusiasts based in the distinctly land-locked town of Eden Prairie, Minnesota have been working on SeaDog since 2002. Following tests off the coasts of Texas and California, it was announced that the device had exceeded expectations by pumping a range of 15,000 to 40,000 gallons of seawater per day in a range of wave conditions. Critics point out that the 17 tonne prototype was in fact delivering roughly enough power to run a single TV set, but it is claimed that 10,000 SeaDogs could generate between 30-1500MW of electricity – depending on the height of waves, which could be a problem since SeaDogs are happiest close to shore, where wave heights are usually modest.

During a recent radio interview a member of the SeaDog team asserted that their machines could power the entire United States. Given the results so far this could be described as *dogged* optimism. In the most recent news, eighteen SeaDog pumps are to be installed near Freeport in Texas to power a desalination plant for bottled water company Renew Blue. Which just so happens to be part of the SeaDog parent company. Publicity ploy or not, SeaDogs are simple beasts who could well be useful in averting the worldwide freshwater crisis.

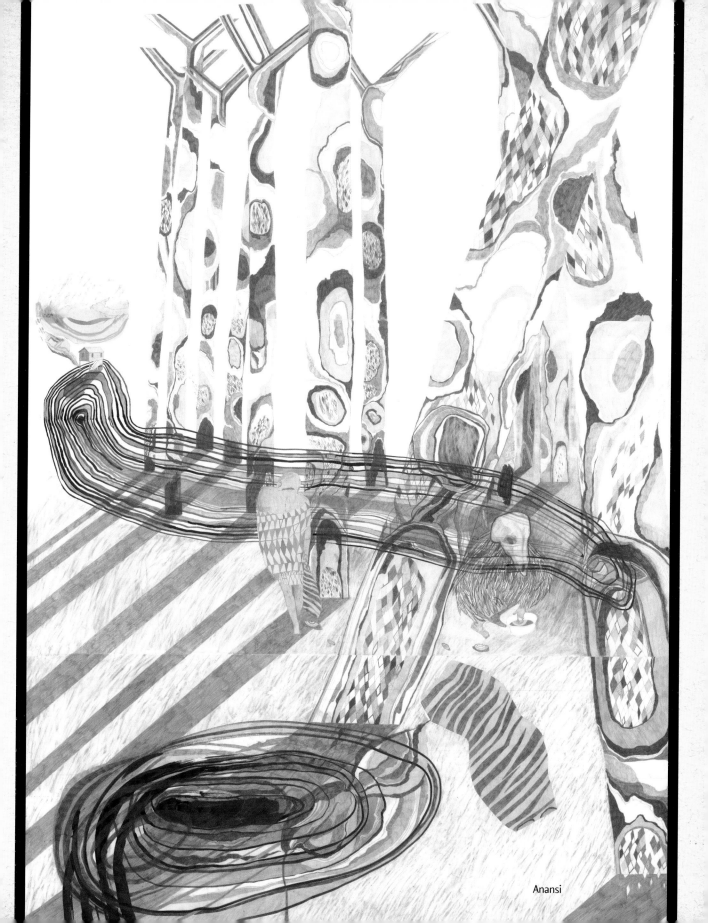

Anansi

IMAGINE a sky filled with balloons that generate electricity. How glorious a sight that would be! This is exactly what is envisaged by Ian Edmonds of Solartran in Brisbane, Australia. His simple concept is based on the same idea as the familiar petrol engine of a car, which works by expanding gases in a piston chamber to create motion that is converted into the rotation of wheels. The pistons move up and down with a stroke of just a few centimetres, but consider instead what would happen with a stroke measuring a few kilometres. Edmonds suggests this could be done by using a hot air balloon that takes advantage of the 65ºc temperature difference between ground and high altitude, to rise up and down in the atmosphere.

But how? A solar thermal collector is used to charge the balloon with hot air so that it rises up to 3km, pulling all the while on a winch to generate electricity. When the balloon cools down in the upper atmosphere it loses buoyancy and descends to the ground to start the cycle all over again. Edmonds estimates that a single 44m diameter balloon could deliver enough power for ten homes, so 200 giant balloons could

produce the same amount of electricity as a small power station. It would be a wonderful sight, if you like balloons. Although on windy days the whole lot would be grounded, which is why the inventor suggests that balloons could be used as a complement to wind powered turbines.

Another concept that involves balloons comes from Sunhope, who propose helium-filled balloons coated in photovoltaic cells, to collect solar power. One balloon measuring several metres in diameter will create the same amount of energy as a small field of solar panels, and is designed to be very low maintenance, with infrastructure composed entirely of a control panel, a helium supply and a power cable. They will be practical for use in deserts, forests and the ocean, and easy to set up in emergency situations where they could be delivered by air. The balloons should last a year without needing maintenance and could be linked in networks. The designers are currently making the balloons as wind resistant as possible by experimenting with size and structure.

HOT AIR BALLOON FARM

Two of Hearts for Amelia's Magazine Shelter Card Quilt

Royal Bank of Sustainability for Amelia's Magazine
and Platform at C Words, Arnolfini

When HELEN DODSWORTH was a child she would shuffle back and forth to the recycling centre across town for an entire day at a time. That's dedication. So it comes as no surprise that this Manchester-based illustrator admires the colours, style and ethics of Hundertwasser. "He was a humanist who believed that people should live in harmony with nature, and these ideals informed all his work. He believed that every roof should have a garden and he designed posters for environmental campaigns such as Plant Trees Avert Nuclear Peril, which I think is a great slogan."

Helen gets excited by quirky children's stories accompanied by beautiful illustrations. "I love stories by Quentin Blake and classics like Where the Wild Things Are. But I like lots of newer books too; Aaaarrgghh! Spider! by Lydia Monks is great. It's about a spider who wants to be a family's pet, but everything he does to win them over just scares them." She likes fantastical stories set in strange landscapes full of odd creatures. "I was really inspired by an exhibition at The Queens Gallery in Buckingham Palace called Amazing Rare Things, which was a collection of beautiful drawings made by European nature artists during the Age of Discovery, when new and exotic countries were being mapped for the first time." Although the drawings were beautifully accurate in many ways they were often surreal in composition, which appealed to Helen immensely. "In one painting by the gentleman gardener Alexander Marshal there is a tiny greyhound sat next to a massive sunflower." Japanese artist Kuniyoshi, the godfather of modern day manga, drew weird and wonderful depictions of animals in the nineteenth century.

"My favourite is the Octopus Games, which includes an octopus doing karate – it's pretty great." She also likes the playful album artwork by Keiichi Tanaami and Pete Fowler for the Super Furry Animals.

Helen graduated in 2001 from the School of Art and Design at Loughborough University , and worked as a printed textile designer for fashion in New York and in Copenhagen, where the design studio bordered Christiana, a community set up in a former military barracks in 1971. This utopian creation affected Helen greatly. "In my ideal vision of the future everyone would pitch in and work together. We would grow all our own food, cycle everywhere and create our own cheap community entertainment. We need to break out of this consumerist cultural hole we've fallen into." Helen has worked with communities since she returned, starting with Pyramid of Arts in Leeds, for people with learning disabilities. "We made a giant bird puppet the size of a house for the Kirkstall Parade, and when we took it out into the streets all the neighbourhood children came out to have a look. Everyone was so happy with what they had achieved – it was a very good looking bird."

She currently works part-time for a similar charity in Manchester called Elizabeth Fitzroy Support, making props and scenery for drama performances, and she also runs screen-printing workshops at Stockport College. "I'm not very good at working into the early hours of the morning to complete stuff, but I managed to do it for this deadline." Helen completed her illustration for the anthology whilst working full tilt on her other projects, managing to turn up a whole new idea based on hot air balloons from an article

posted online by the New Scientist. The image was created by scanning line drawings into Photoshop where she colours and composes them. "I like answering briefs that inspire and communicate ideas in a positive way," she says.

Over the years Helen has successfully distanced herself from the fashion industry. "I fell into the fashion world but it didn't suit me. I'm not a big fan of all the questionable ethics associated with it." She felt limited by the scope of printed textiles. "I've drawn all the flowers I could possibly ever draw and I wanted to try something new. I missed drawing just for the fun of it." When she saw the work of Jim Stoten in issue 06 of Amelia's Magazine it gave her the kickstart she needed

to diversify into illustration. From flowers to bugs and butterflies it wasn't long before Helen realised that she was adding faces to her images, making them into characters, sometimes inspired by television shows, often by favourite animals such as the endangered Crested Black Macaque monkey. "It's on the endangered species list, and the thought of such a beautiful animal disappearing forever is awful." She muses over the idea of creating an Illustrators Against Extinction campaign group. "We could do a range of illustrations about endangered animals and make them into a short story in a pamphlet. That would be fun to do."

helen dodsworth

BioWave Power

Biomimicry looks at the way things are done in the natural world and then looks at how a design can work in harmony with its surroundings instead of attempting to bludgeon the elements into submission. The single biggest problem for wave energy devices is how to survive in the extremely variable and hostile ocean environment. But there are lots of things that thrive in the sea, seaweed being a prime example. The motion of kelp on the seafloor is designed to 'go with the flow' – a fact that has not escaped BioPower Systems of Sydney, Australia. Their BioWave system sways in the wave currents, oscillating freely on a slender multi-pronged patented BioBase that takes its cue from nature. Unlike conventional systems it doesn't have a main shaft but instead has many 'roots' – a mechanism for mooring that is used by large sea plants such as kelp. The resulting motion is converted into electrical power which is transmitted along the seabed. In extreme conditions the 'kelp' simply lies flat until trouble has passed.

The BioStream unit is a similar concept but designed with tidal currents in mind: it mimics the kind of fish tail seen on shark, tuna, and mackerel. Most fish generate thrust via lateral movements of their body and the tail fin, but the species that adopt the Thunniform swimming mode – favoured by high speed long distance swimmers – derive nearly all of their propulsion from a relatively large crescent shaped tail. They are therefore experts at harnessing the power of the ocean for fast and effective movement; the perfect inspiration for a machine that sits in shallow tidal waters, and like a weathervane changes pitch as the waves push around it. This shape is known to be 90% efficient at converting the propulsive force of water into energy.

There are several benefits to these designs; because BioPower units are light and do not need to be bolted down with hefty bases they are much cheaper to install. The gentle oscillation of the 'fronds' and 'tail' means that fish are far less likely to get smacked with the device, as the waves will push both in the same direction.

A single 25m high BioWave unit is being put into operation off King Island, Tasmania, and a collaboration has just been announced with the City of San Francisco to trial the machines five miles into the Pacific Ocean. Each device will produce 1MW, and 'kelp' forests will be able to generate between 10MW and 100MW.

Aquamarine Power of Edinburgh has also looked to the natural world for its Oyster unit, which sits on the ocean floor and features a hinged lid that flaps back and forth to pump seawater ashore to drive a turbine. A full-scale test at the European Marine Energy Centre Orkney began in 2009 and the results so far are good. But it doesn't look half as beautiful as the floating fronds of kelp.

JAMES NICHOLLS lives in Bromley, a suburb on the borders of London, where he shares a studio with the two other members of the Tiptoe Collective. Since graduating in 2006 he has pursued a freelance career in illustration whilst supplementing his income with graphic design.

Tell me how you got into illustration...

From a very young age I enjoyed drawing and wanted to pursue a career in art, so I studied graphic design at Norwich School of Art and Design where I decided to specialise in illustration. In 2008 I formed Tiptoe with fellow graduates Ian Caulkett and Mark Whittle;

I think we all had to work on our own for a while to find out exactly how tough illustration can be, but I wish we'd set it up earlier because we've all enjoyed more success since we decided to work as a collective.

What prompted you to set up the collective?

We thought that having a joint website and sending out publicity together would be easier and less intimidating than going it totally alone. It's also had the benefit of helping us to stay motivated and involved with each other's work. Since forming we've been commissioned as a collective to collaborate on a few different projects, including the creation of some large – scale illustrations for the walls of the new headquarters of Dubai based advertising agency, Mojo. The project took approximately two weeks to develop and plan in the UK, before heading to Dubai for a week to create the work on a ninety square metre wall. It was quite a lot of pressure to complete it on time, but we knew we had to make our flights home! The concept was based on the importance of water – there is nothing but empty desert around the city so all the food has to be shipped in, which is very

expensive and of course completely unsustainable. For another big project we took over the reception area of advertising agency AMV BBDO and transformed it into a Christmas wonderland based on a fairground from yesteryear complete with toys, presents and music. It wouldn't really have been possible for any of us to do such large – scale illustrations alone so it offered an invaluable experience of working as part of a team, combining very different styles of illustration to make them work together.

When do you work on your illustrations?

I mostly work on my illustrations in the evening and weekends, as I have to work around my day job. I'm a graphic designer in a marketing department for an electronics company, but I'm lucky because the hours are quite flexible and it's a creative environment which informs my freelance work. Plus the experience of working in marketing helps me to market my own work, and the graphic design aspect gives me vital experience in producing work suitable for print.

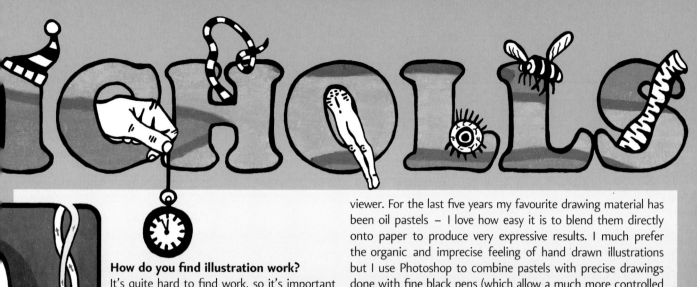

How do you find illustration work?

It's quite hard to find work, so it's important to put it out there on my website, in online showcases, and through actually sending examples out to art directors. A lot of the time luck is very important. Other than with friends I met on my degree, the only real networking I do is over the internet via social networking sites like Facebook and Flickr. Flickr is probably the best place to visit because there's so much work on there and groups to join. It's a good place to find out about competitions and magazines that want submissions.

What do you think inspires your style?

Two major influences on me are the Fauves and Pop Art. I regularly visit galleries in London and the internet is vital for finding out what else is going on in the world. An underlying theme of my work is nature, and I often portray diagrammatic representations of animals, the human body and plants.

How do you create your illustrations?

The most important aspect of my work is colour. I like bold contrasts that get the attention of the viewer and I'm particularly interested in how colours and shapes can be used together to produce images that at first glance may not be entirely obvious to the

viewer. For the last five years my favourite drawing material has been oil pastels – I love how easy it is to blend them directly onto paper to produce very expressive results. I much prefer the organic and imprecise feeling of hand drawn illustrations but I use Photoshop to combine pastels with precise drawings done with fine black pens (which allow a much more controlled attention to detail), and I think it's working quite well. Computers are especially useful for coming up with concepts and compositions quickly, to digitally collage hand drawn pieces together and for correcting colours and cropping finished pieces.

What are your views on sustainable living?

I'm passionate about living sustainably and not only has it influenced my work over the years but I'm constantly looking for new ways to live more lightly. I always recycle when I can, I don't have a car even though I can drive and I use public transport. I think it's important that sustainable choices be made easy for the general public. During my research for this project I learnt just how many technologies are actually being developed to produce renewable energy. Not enough of them are getting the support they really need to become mass produced and commercially viable, even though most of them could be. Governments really need to step in more to help out because the ideas and technolo- gies already exist, they just haven't been implemented yet.

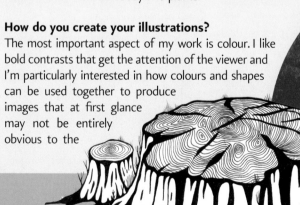

KITESHIP

KITES *have always held a grasp over peoples' imaginations, and that fascination is fast making kite power the holy grail of alternative energy.*

Some might note that not much has changed down the centuries. During the 1820's English school teacher George Pocock devised a flying chair attached to a kite which could haul his small daughter 80m up in the air, leading directly to his Charvolant invention; a carriage pulled by steerable kites. He later took his family for a glamourous three day cruise in the Bristol channel aboard a kite powered boat. Over in Australia the trustafarian Lawrence Hargrave used his inheritance to perfect a tiered box kite system that was also capable of lifting large weights, and his developments led directly

to manned flight as we know it. The flamboyant stuntman Samuel Cody – born in Iowa, known as the King of the Cowboys and obsessed with kites – crossed the English Channel in a kite-powered boat in 1903.

Since then materials have improved somewhat with the arrival of super-strong plastic and light-weight foil. By the 1970's young men who were kite-surfing, kite-sailing and even kite-skating by day were dreaming of kite engines by night. Dean Jordan, (a professional kite flyer since the 1980's), studied under the guidance of master kite designer Peter Lynn in New Zealand and together with engineer Dean Culp formed KiteShip in California in 1996. Kites initially made for sport and pleasure boats are now being designed to pull tankers. Known as VLFFS, these Very Large Free Flying Sails are as big as a football field, fly 100m above the sea and save 15-30% on fuel costs. Across the pond in Europe SkySails offers a very similar technology; and proved that their kite sail could successfully substitute 20% of the engine's power when the container cargo ship MA Beluga sailed from Germany to Venezuela in 2008. They have been steadily retrofitting commercial ships with their system ever since.

But why not just stick to normal sails? Well, kites have a far larger surface area, offer more control, and can access more wind energy at higher elevations. Whilst airplanes may get a lot of press for carbon emissions, most of our goods actually travel around the world by sea, and those ships are responsible for a great deal of carbon emissions, so anything that might cut those has got to be a good thing. And the plans for kite usage don't stop there: designs are afoot for kites to lift heavy things in remote places: to divert dangerous icebergs, tow oil rigs and perhaps even explore distant planets. Maybe.

Rainforests are FOUND ON EVERY continent across Earth, except ANTARCTICA.

RAINFORESTS ACT as the WORLD'S THERMOSTAT by REGULATING TEMPS AND WEATHER PATTERNS.

AT THE CURRENT RATE OF TROPICAL FOREST LOSS, 5-10% OF TROPICAL RAIN FOREST species WILL BE LOST PER DECADE.

MORE THAN 56,000 SQUARE MILES OF NATURAL RAINFOREST IS LOST EVERY YEAR.

EVERY SECOND, a slice of the rainforest the size of A football FIELD is mowed down. THAT'S 86,400 FOOTBALL FIELDS EVERY YEAR.

ORIGINALLY, 6 MILLION SQUARE MILES of Tropical Rainforest EXISTED WORLDWIDE.

BEFORE 1500 AD, there were approximately 6 MILLION INDIGENOUS people LIVING IN THE BRAZILIAN AMAZON. THERE ARE NOW ONLY 250,000 PEOPLE.

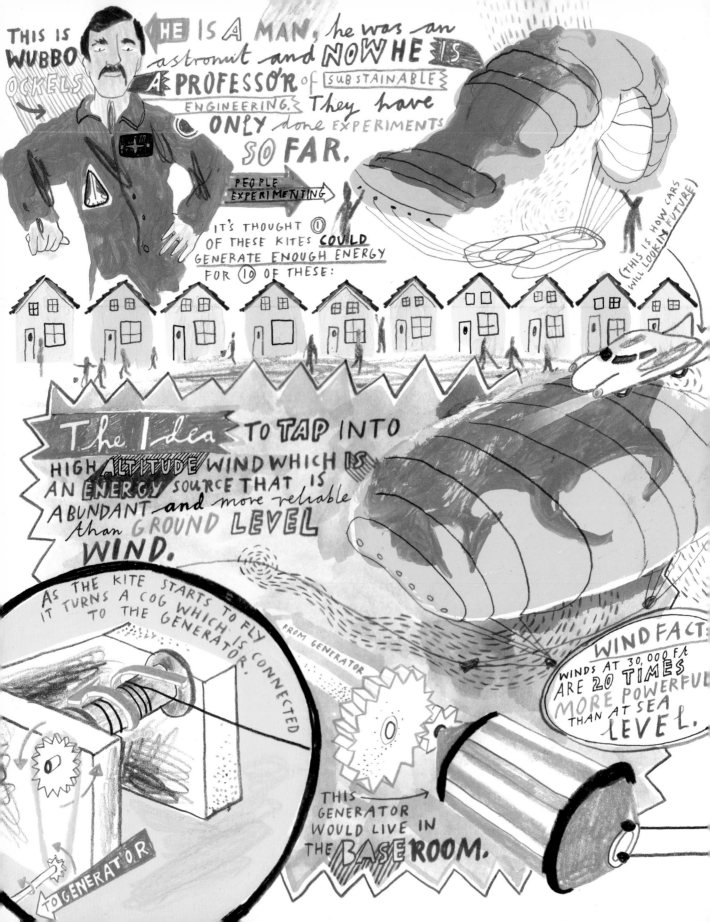

THIS IS WUBBO OCKELS

HE IS A MAN, he was an astronaut and NOW HE IS A PROFESSOR of SUBSTAINABLE ENGINEERING. They have ONLY done EXPERIMENTS SO FAR.

PEOPLE EXPERIMENTING →

IT'S THOUGHT ① OF THESE KITES COULD GENERATE ENOUGH ENERGY FOR ⑩ OF THESE:

(THIS IS HOW CARS WILL LOOK IN FUTURE)

The Idea TO TAP INTO HIGH ALTITUDE WIND WHICH IS AN ENERGY SOURCE THAT IS ABUNDANT and more reliable than GROUND LEVEL WIND.

AS THE KITE STARTS TO FLY IT TURNS A COG WHICH IS CONNECTED TO THE GENERATOR.

FROM GENERATOR

TO GENERATOR

THIS GENERATOR WOULD LIVE IN THE BASE ROOM.

WIND FACT! WINDS AT 30,000 ft ARE 20 TIMES MORE POWERFUL THAN AT SEA LEVEL.

Vintage Clothing Party, Spindle

JESS **WILSON** sits back in her chair in a nondescript coffee shop not far from her workplace and flat in Islington, London, and laughs as she reminisces about the year spent – by her own admission – drawing illustrations of Dennis The Menace "pretty solidly." Was he some kind of muse, an inspiration to the burgeoning artist? "I don't know about that, I just liked to draw him," she deadpans. Jess is not one for hyperbole. She creates art because she likes to – and because she's good at it. Nuff said.

Neither does she care to be part of the achingly cool London art scene. No, not this girl clad in a baggy knitted jumper complete with doggie motif. Instead she prefers to spend her off-duty time following her beloved football team, Ipswich Town (but don't hold that against her), heading down the local, or challenging her five flat mates (all uni friends) to a game of Guitar Hero – the medium to hard level, she is keen to point out.

Looking back at her illustration for issue 06 of Amelia's Magazine a couple of years ago Jess comments that her style has got much more intricate and intense over the years. "It used to be all about the squiggle, but since I got a light box I use way more patterns because it's so easy to trace out images again and again," she explains. She can spend a lot of time on an illustration. "I like to progress, throw a new pattern in here or a shape over there, until I'm happy with it." Her trademark style gives a respectful nod to the style and format of comic books, not least because she tends to make good use of text. "I guess I like to tell a humorous story... but it's quite weird that I use text since I'm really bad at spelling – I did that test at university and got a free computer out of it." Free Willy the whale makes an appearance on her main illustration and she concedes "that's where I went off on a random tangent."

At Bucks New University (she graduated in 2006) Jess learnt much about her artistic strengths and weaknesses, explaining "The more I got involved in graphic design the more I realised that

I prefer and feel more comfortable doing illustration." She is not that keen on computers; "I can deal without them, I much prefer to sit and draw," but admits that working four days a week as a design production assistant at a publishing company has developed her technical abilities and enables Jess to work on commissions and private projects on her day off. "I make books and go around stalls trying to sell them. The last one looked at scams and tricks and I experimented with loads of different print processes such as photocopying, screen-printing, mono-printing, stencils and die-cuts." She sells her zines at London book fairs Handmade & Bound, London Zine Symposium and Publish And Be Damned and has just set up a small publishing enterprise with fellow illustrator Ryan Todd. "I'm currently working on a zine about drag racing at Santa Pod. I went there for a day out with a friend who shares my sense of humour and we met loads of interesting people." Inspiration for anecdotal stories increasingly comes from the internet as well. "People get up to such strange things," she laughs.

Her National Anthem image was in response to a brief from the East End Arts Club (a collective that promotes affordable limited edition prints) to illustrate a 'hidden gem'. "Very few people are aware of all six verses of the National Anthem so I thought it might be a good idea to draw them out." She is now working on an animation of the entire song. "I don't know why this has become such an obsession," she chuckles. "It's probably because I find it funny." Vintage Clothing Party was done for the online literary magazine Spindle. The commission demanded that she show how vintage clothing could be reused and given a new life. "I really enjoyed creating a story for every item at the party," she says.

In her kite illustration Jess chose to represent the life and times of Wubbo Ockels, the Dutch physicist and astronaut who expounds the use of kites as an inexpensive way to harvest the enormous energy available in the wind. "Being a visual person I was straightaway attracted to the kite. I'd never thought of the kite

Two of Hearts for Amelia's Magazine Shelter Card Quilt

being used in this way before, but really it's quite an obvious contraption." It transpires that near her parent's house (in the middle of nowhere) plans to build a wind turbine farm are being vehemently opposed by a few locals. "From my reading I get the impression that kites are a lot quieter than wind turbines so maybe they could provide an alternative solution."

A keen recycler, Jess eschews cars in favour of her trusty bike, and the freedom of cycling everywhere suits her. "I like to follow my own timetable," she says as she fastens her helmet in preparation for the journey home.

London, UK

www.jesswilson.co.uk

Everything is Connected for Amelia's Magazine issue 10

Enchanted Forest for Amelia's Magazine issue 06

BURNING BIOMASS to create energy is as old as humanity, and in many places it's still very popular on a small scale. Now it's time to reappraise this idea in a much wider way.

In 1816 Scottish clergyman Robert Stirling invented a revolutionary engine that creates power by transferring gas between hot and cold zones, using the expansion and contraction to drive a shaft. Because there is no explosive combustion it is very quiet, and, being sealed, needs little maintenance. But the best part of all is that very little heat is lost, thus making it super efficient. For many years Stirling's invention has languished on the sidelines. But we can no longer ignore the shocking amount of energy that is lost from conventional power stations: up to 60% vanishes straight out of those iconic cooling towers and 3.5% is then lost in transition through the distribution network. And it just isn't possible for huge centralised power stations to share any heat with the surrounding community.

So Stirling's ideas are now being reappraised for use in small scale Combined Heat and Power (CHP) plants. Which are also in themselves an old idea. In the US Thomas Edison was an early evangelist for CHP, responsible in 1882 for the building of the world's first commercial power station, which produced both electricity and heat that was used to warm neighbouring buildings. Unfortunately for the US and the UK fortune (and regulations) favoured centralised power production and so whilst CHP plants are very popular in the Netherlands and Denmark – who use them to obtain half their energy – they are scarce in most countries despite their suitability for cities, where CHP plants can be small, extremely quiet and unobtrusive. For example, CHP plants can be hidden in town centre car parks and most residents don't even know they're there.

But in what way is CHP renewable? Well, sometimes it isn't, but a CHP plant can operate at 95% efficiency as compared to an average of 38% efficiency for conventional energy production, so it is a step in the right direction. It is possible to make CHP almost completely sustainable, by either burning local waste biomass material such as sawmill offcuts and straw, or by harvesting sustainable biomass. Additionally, a range of diverse fuels can be used in the same boilers so that the fuel type can be altered according to availability. The most obviously abundant and fully sustainable form of fuel is of course the oldest one of all: wood. Fast growing trees can be grown and harvested in short cycles or certain varieties can be coppiced, one of the longest practiced techniques in the world. Trees such as willow and poplar are coppiced by cutting them back to the stump so that the new shoots can be harvested in a regular cycle. During medieval times this was the primary source of fuel in the UK and for many people around the world, it continues to be. It is estimated that one square kilometre of well-coppiced trees could yield 1MW of electricity, enough for around 1000 homes and perfect for wildlife too. No wonder some of the most ancient ideas in existence are finally making a comeback.

Two of Hearts for Amelia's Magazine Shelter Card Quilt

ART BY JUSTIN WALLIS

www.milkbbi.co.nr   Arkansas, US

TAKE US THROUGH A TYPICAL WORKDAY WITH YOU.
Well, right when I wake up I always know whether or not the day is gonna be productive. When it is, I wake up early, eat a pop tart and drink some strawberry banana juice. Ya know, it just feels natural and right to wake up with the sun for a fresh start. Then I make some sweet tea and take a whole gallon to my bedroom to have by my side while I draw. When I finally start to do something I have to work on it until I can't do anymore or until I'm out of sweet tea. When I finish it, I find a friend or go onto the internet for some kind of feedback or reassurance. It's great for super diverse and immediate comments. There is   no doubt in my mind when I feel like something is finished, so it can be hard to go back to it.

AH, IF ONLY WE COULD POWER THE WORLD WITH SWEET TEA!
HOW DO YOU WORK?
I almost always do my work in my bedroom because it's so comfortable in there and I feel like I'm stepping into my own little cocoon. My workspace is a pretty big mess, but I definitely know where everything is. And I love it; it's where I keep all my treasures. I have so much stuff piled everywhere it's kinda like a dirty ol' flea market but I like to be around comforting, familiar things. I draw with basic things like pens, pencils and markers, but to change things up I use stickers and highlighters as well. If reality were no object I would paint with natural objects, such as an apple or a branch – it would be great to create their exact colours.

DO YOU HAVE TO JUGGLE ART WITH OTHER RESPONSIBILITIES?
Not really, nothing out of the ordinary. I'm really dedicated to my art, 100%. When I was a little kid I dreamed of being an artist. It's the only thing I ever wanted to be so of course I aim to be a full-time illustrator! The rejection can be hard though, and I'd love to try other things in the art field.

WHERE DO YOU DRAW INSPIRATION FROM?
A lot of the things that inspire me are from childhood interests or things I drew as a kid. I feel really close to those things – they are my roots – so it feels good to grow from them. I really liked an animated manga show called FLCL when I was younger so sometimes when I need ideas I play the DVDs again while I think. I don't even watch them, I just listen and kinda glance over the screen. I've seen the episodes so many times that I know them back to front so I don't need to! But the familiar feelings and memories are very inspiring. I like 60's art too, not the psychedelic stuff but those kitsch velvet paintings of cute animals and macramé wall hangings. I hope my illustrations create the feeling of youthful innocence and togetherness.

NOW ON TO THE TOPIC OF THE ENVIRONMENT...
TELL US ABOUT YOURS.

I was born, raised and still currently live in Arkansas, in the United States. Being a part of the 'bible belt' it's definitely not known for its diversity or place in the art world, which is why I don't plan on staying too long. But it does have character. Arkansas is known as The Natural State and that's pretty much what it is. For sure there are plenty of mountains, caves and state parks! It's also the only US state where diamonds are mined and you can even dig for them yourself in one state park. One of the longest pedestrian/bike only bridges is also in Arkansas. Overall it is a quiet place and the people here are content with what they have and don't want to change it... ever. You might think that people here would be concerned about the environment but it doesn't seem to be the case. I don't see anyone making many efforts to do things differently. Strange really.

DID YOU KNOW ANYTHING ABOUT CHP BEFORE YOU STARTED DRAWING?

Not at all! But I learned about it through lots of intense googling! Really – I had to read and read about it until I was familiar with how it works so I could interpret it in my own way. I thought it was really interesting and inspiring that a town or building could be responsible for powering itself and the whole process would be so much closer to home. It seems so easy and so clear. I think everyone should get started right away. For this illustration, I figured the best way to show the entire process would be to use a chain/assembly line sorta deal and spread it across both pages. I added in little quirky things and lots of colours to stay away from the generic factory image and make it something fun too!

WHERE DID THE NAME MILKBBI COME FROM?

There are too many other folks called Justin Wallis out there, even ones with the same middle name as me! There is even another designer who has my name, so I had to do something different, to stand out. I picked up the nickname Milk in high school, and I like the way people in old movies used to call each other... baby.

WHAT IS YOUR VIEW OF COMPUTERS?

I don't use the computer much for my artwork, only to tweak colours a little or to bring something to life. Like the animation of my dog Lucy. I like to take photos of her but to be honest she is definitely more of a distraction than a helper; my dad found her abandoned in a house and she is really tiny and weird, we just play around. But of course the internet is easily the best place to connect/collaborate with all my favourite artists. I guess because I live in an area where there isn't much art going on I use the internet to reach out to people and get my work out there. I make friends with artists in other countries and have started a collaboration with four of my favourite online illustrators; Inés Estrada from Mexico City, Lauren Albert from New York, Ginette Lapalme from Toronto and Michael Cuccia from New Orleans. Each of us has made a line drawing which we then copy and send out in the mail to everyone, so that we can all add our own colour and decoration. The eventual plan is to create a colouring book that is a big new melting pot of ideas! I'm super excited to see how all our styles mix up and mash together.

www.karolinschnoor.com

London, UK

ILLUSTRATOR KAROLIN SCHNOOR came from Germany to study on the BA in Graphic and Media Design at London College of Communications, specialising in illustration. She lives in a "really nice flat with great light" which also serves as a studio space but "it would probably also be a good idea to get out of the house once in a while, just for sanity's sake."

When does inspiration tend to strike?

With some projects I can sit down and just get started, but sometimes inspiration is a little more sneaky and it comes out at unexpected moments. I find that it really helps to think a project to death and then when I've immersed myself in it I give myself a little break and a good idea will come. Public transport is a good place for this; something about moving forward even if it's in slow London traffic. It gives the illusion of progression which I don't get when I'm stuck at my desk.

How do you get to work?

My work process is very straight forward: I have a stack of white paper, some sharp pencils, a selection of fine-liners and my trusted scanner! I love drawing but I don't like mess so all my work is quite flat and precise. I have a big sketchbook where I do very rough idea sketches and measurements and I use Photoshop for colouring in. I really like the limitations of the screen-printing technique: the little tricks that are used to make colour layers work together and the compositions more interesting. I

think this is where some of the flatness in my work originates from.

Has your German upbringing affected your style?

My grandmother was a seamstress so she was always surrounded by patterned materials and knitted blankets – I think I probably absorbed this aesthetic on an unconscious level and it still influences me today. My mother drew pictures with me all the time and I was obsessed with all kinds of books from an early age, poring over the intricate folksy patterns and traditional woodcuts for hours at a time, always saving my favourite illustration for last. I think this informs my love of flat shapes and illustration: there's nothing like the printed page.

What else has influenced you?

One of the first illustrators who had a profound effect on me was Aubrey Beardsley; he produced both beautiful and controversial work without compromising either. I am also a big graphic novel fan because I like the idea of illustrations working within a narrative framework. Style is one thing but the ability to make that style work for a story is something I really admire, particularly the work of comic artists Chris Ware, Craig Thompson, Daniel Clowes and Art Spiegelman. On the other side of the historical spectrum I really love Gustav Klimt and the Pre-Raphaelite painter John William Waterhouse for their opulent beauty and the way they used detail and decoration without taking away from the atmosphere they were creating. And just to balance out the fact that I have named only men so far, I am also a big fan of Sanna Annukka's work: she's great.

Is there a scene amongst illustrators?

I think there is, and it's great that illustration has gained power and recognition over the last few years. There are a lot of prominent figures who are able to combine good work with good self-promotion but I am only just learning to 'put myself out there'. It seems so far removed from what I do at home at my drawing table. I love the internet because it's so nice and non-confrontational. I am still in touch with a few people from my illustration class so we are cultivating a mini-scene of our own. Very mini. I like the idea of working with others and I think it gets easier the further your disciplines are apart. I don't know how good I would be at collaborating with another illustrator unless they had a completely different style. I'd really like to do some textile work or translate my drawings into moving image and I'm also a huge fan of Coralie Bickford-Smith's design work at Penguin so at the moment she is top of my list of dream collaborators .

What was your experience of university?

As part of my degree I spent time at the École Estienne in Paris, where I had long studio sessions with a teacher who actually sat down and talked to me at length about a detail of my drawing. The students were extremely skilled because there was a lot of emphasis on traditional techniques such as litho printing and traditional letterpress, but it wasn't as conceptual and context driven as LCC so it was the perfect counterbalance. I also did an internship in Berlin at the illustration and design studio Apfel Zet, and whenever I get disillusioned about a project I remember how much they enjoyed their work and what awesome people they were – down to earth and not at all pretentious, just really serious about doing good work. It was a great experience and continues to motivate me.

Do you work full time in illustration?

I'm freelance so I end up mixing illustration with graphic design work which is good because they complement each other. It's good to be able to go from doing a drawing to working on a website or doing a print project. I don't feel like I need to choose and I am really enjoying doing a bit of everything at the moment. When it comes to design I am much more open to suggestions, while with illustration it feels more personal. I have a core group of critics that I trust and like to get feedback from but I am also very stubborn and mostly stick to my initial instincts. I really don't like telling others about projects before they have been confirmed because I'm afraid of jinxing them!

What have you been working on recently?

I've contributed a few images to blogposts on the Amelia's Magazine website because I found the articles interesting. The selection of illustrators is really varied and engaging and it's also enjoyable to do things with a quick turn-around whilst working on projects to a longer time-scale; it's good to mix things up. I talked the owners of a restaurant in Folkestone into letting me design their website, which involved a lot of photography as well as illustration so it was quite a fun, diverse project. And I took part in a small group show at the Ritzy in Brixton, London with some LCC alumni; all work had to be inspired by a film so I chose Annie Hall, which was probably a mistake because it's hard to do something meaningful from a film you really love. I drew a lobster heart because lobsters form the basis for a romantic scene. I really enjoyed designing the flyers in cinema ticket style; we printed them on sugar paper for an authentic feel and gave everyone popcorn at the private view. It was a good night.

What are your favourite things to draw?

I always end up drawing girls and trees. It's hard to stay away from illustration clichés like birds, they're just a lot of fun to draw! I think though that it's mostly shapes and colours that I get excited about. I feel very immersed in city life so nature takes on a more mystical importance. And the colours are just better. I recently went on a big walk in the Devon hills and there were all these greens and purples and rusty reds. But people and their interactions with each other are the best source for ideas and inspiration, especially overheard conversations. My very favourite thing is squinting and chipping away at a drawing until it feels finished: it's very satisfying to feel that a balance has been struck and a composition is complete.

How did you choose which technology to illustrate?

I wanted to do something that used water as its power source because it makes so much sense to me. You can literally see and hear the energy that is produced by the sea and the next logical step is to harvest it. I was also very impressed by the fact that SeaGen had been produced and tested and had even been connected to the electrical grid. The sheer number of households it could power was a deciding factor: each turbine could supply one thousand homes. My concern is not that we aren't ready to produce alternative energies but rather that the people pulling the strings have other vested interests. I know we have the intelligence and the materials to live more responsibly but other political factors get in the way. But it's encouraging to see how much work is being done and to know that things are possible.

STRANGFORD LOUGH in Northern Ireland is the site of one of the earliest tidal mills in the world: the Nendrum monastery mill dating to over 1300 years ago. It is surely not entirely coincidental that the world's first large scale commercial tidal turbine has been installed at the mouth of the same lough: the best place to put a tidal mill or a tidal turbine is where the tidal rise is high and the tidal current is strong.

The SeaGen tidal turbine, connected to the grid in July 2008, is four times more powerful than any other tidal stream generator in the world. Built in the same Belfast dock as the Titanic, it took two weeks to install because, ironically, the team had to overcome the very tides that are now powering the turbines. The machine weighs 300 tonnes and has two rotors which act as water windmills, each 16m in diameter and revolving 10-15 times a minute. They can flip over to take advantage of the ebb and flow of the tides which form a wall of water 27m high travelling at speeds of up to 16kph. The turbines are supported on a thick column sunk into the sea-bed and can be slid out of the water for inspection and repair.

Ecological impacts have been especially well considered, with a promise to stop operating if wildlife is affected. To establish a good environmental record the SeaGen device was deliberately sited near a seal colony and tests are being conducted to check that dolphin sonar capabilities are not affected by the cavita-tion noises from the blades. Only after one year of continuous successful operation was the company given the all-clear to continue without marine mammal observers on board and onshore at all times.

The SeaGen machine is the vision of a single pioneering engineer, Peter Fraenkel, who has been working in the renewable energy industry since the 1970's. It was developed by a small West country company who trialled a smaller prototype called SeaFlow off the coast of Devon for several years. The Irish SeaGen machine is rated at 1.2MW but is now consistently generating more energy than was predicted: more than enough power for over 1000 homes. It will operate for five years, after which there are plans to install seven SeaGen machines off the Isle of Anglesey in Wales, in a fast-flowing tidal area called the Skerries.

Half of all the tidal stream potential in Europe is around the UK. It has been estimated that the tidal streams at a single site, the Pentland Firth at the northern tip of Scotland, could generate up to 25% of the electricity requirements of the UK. An astonishing 2.5 cubic metres of water – enough to fill 1000 Olympic swimming pools – rushes through the Firth every second. The engineering challenge of installing turbines in this turbulent current boggles the mind.

Lobster Heart, Ritzy

Time Out

No.11, Folkestone

Amelia's Magazine, Earth Section

Two of Hearts for Amelia's Magazine Shelter Card Quilt

Kate Morgan

www.illustratorkate.co.uk   Loughborough, UK

SHEFFIELD BORN KATE MORGAN graduated from Loughborough University in 2007 and works in youth arts when she isn't creating illustrations. She would love to illustrate a children's book and see it in on the shelves of libraries and shops.

WORKING WITH YOUNG PEOPLE.

Choosing to study illustration was definitely the right choice for me, I was so happy when I discovered I could do it as a degree. I loved sharing feedback with my fellow illustration students in a group studio. After graduating I had no money so I moved back home to Sheffield where I began volunteering for a community arts charity and found that I really liked working with young people in the arts. After a year I was offered a position helping to devise and deliver fun art activities for young people in a disadvantaged area of the city, and when the contract finished I moved back to Loughborough. Now I work part time as a youth arts worker for Charnwood Arts, where I help teenagers who are at risk of offending improve their skills through one-to-one art activities. I also work as an artist at a school in Leicester and I continue to illustrate.

SKETCHING THE SKY.

I like to use quite a small sketchbook where I work through all my thought processes using little thumbnail compositions and trial colour schemes. I paint the separate elements and scan them, then put everything together and neaten it up in Photoshop. I'm currently working on an idea for an illustrated poem about an invisible switch that you can carry around and press whenever you want to disappear. My work focuses on shapes, textures and colour. I like using colour to evoke an immediate mood and atmosphere for the viewer so they are drawn in and start to notice all the small less obvious details that give depth and perspective. I particularly love to illustrate houses, people, skies and the sea. At the moment I'm working on paintings as well as illustration. For these I translate digital compositions onto canvas in acrylics, and add bits of collage to get a textured look.

A CUP OF TEA AND A GOOD BOOK.

I love thinking about the day ahead whilst drinking my first cup of tea and munching on my cereal. I've recently discovered the joy of baking and I go running a few times a week; I always feel really happy afterwards. I'm inspired by the world around me and often find myself wondering how to depict a situation in an illustration, for instance when I'm reading a good book I sometimes sketch the characters and environments as I imagine them to look. I love the detail that Shaun Tan uses in his illustrations to get across a character and their situation and I'm a big fan of the way that John Burningham uses different media in his illustrations.

ADVICE ON GETTING ADVICE.

My friend is an illustrator and she lives round the corner so we often meet up to do a show and tell of our illustration work, which is great. A group of us have also set up a blog called Roar Talent where we set each other briefs and put up work in progress so we can offer each other advice and feedback. It's really important to keep producing artwork, send samples off to magazines, enter competitions and get feedback from fellow creatives. The Association of Illustrators is a good online resource and I surround myself with images of work that I like, so that if I have a dry spell I can look through them and feel more inspired.

ENVISAGING THE FUTURE.

One of the problems with renewable energy is that lots of people dislike the way it looks, but imagine using your garden to take power from the sun and convert it into power for your home: you would be the envy of all the neighbours. So I had this idea to make solar panel sunflowers; they would last all year round, look bright and cheerful and never need watering! For the Selsam turbine I used a very limited colour palette so that the viewer won't be distracted away from the focal point and I particularly enjoyed creating the logo because there were so many different elements to consider. I realised that I could make the turbines look like they were taking off from the sea into the sky like sails on a boat and I found it an enjoyable challenge to put my own stamp on the technology.

HAPPINESS AND TRANSFORMATION.

I think that if people went outside and appreciated green spaces more, then everyone would be a lot happier. The world would be a better place if we had more community areas where everyone could grow food, exercise, get fresh air and create murals. Art has an incredible power to transform the meaning of a subject – a block of text is uniform but an image can communicate in so many different ways. Ten illustrators will give you ten very different interpretations of a subject, and that's what I love about illustration.

Despite promoting himself with possibly the worst website in the history of the universe, lone inventor Doug Selsam is clearly onto something. Amongst his steadily proliferating ideas is an astonishingly simple design based on the mantra More Rotors Equals More Power.

The commercial wind turbines with which we are most familiar were perfected in the 1920's when it was clearly realised that the blades must be designed like wings, using the aerofoil idea to capture power through lift without causing disruptive eddies. But perhaps this design is still not as good as it could be. The standard commercial turbine features three long blades rotating on a horizontal axis and driving a generator via a complex gear box, which is needed to translate the relatively slow rotation of the blades into the rapid rotation needed for efficient generation of electricity. All of this is then mounted on a tall tower. Today's largest wind farms are the size of small towns, lumbering turbines 30 stories tall marching across the landscape with blades the size of 747 wings. These behemoths produce a great deal of power, but manufacturing, transporting, installing and maintaining so much structural steel is both expensive and difficult.

There may be a different way of doing things. Doug Selsam of Fullerton, California claims that he can deliver the same amount of wind power for just 10% of the weight of a conventional turbine. He achieves this result by getting rid of the gear box and the tower. Instead his Sky Serpent design uses a flexible shaft 'like a giant fishing pole' that shifts and moves with the wind currents: like a tree bending in the wind. The multiple small rotors along the length of the stalk operate in a similar manner to a flock of geese, utilising (instead of trying to avoid) the eddies caused by their neighbours, to spin faster. Because the small rotors spin so quickly they are able to drive a generator directly, with the added bonus of acting like gyroscopes to stabilise the driveshaft where they are attached.

Amongst his many ideas Doug suggests the Sky Serpent for use as an offshore superturbine, springing out of a moored floating base that can rotate in a similar way to the human spine so that the turbines won't twist and spin out of control. In an ingenious answer to stormy weather, the turbine base fills with water to submerge it safely beneath the ocean's surface until calmer waters return. Fantastical photore-alistic images commissioned from Dreamworks animator Michael Sanchez show the Sky Serpent dwarfing the passing tanker ships as they spin so fast they are barely visible (another bonus). The addition of a blimp at the tip of the stalk makes the turbine even more stable and effective.

Doug has dreamed of turbines for several decades, but it wasn't until 1999 – after an extended hiatus as a heavy-metal guitarist – that he settled properly into his ideas. These days he manufactures all his turbines in his suburban garage and tests the Sky Serpent in a makeshift wind tunnel in the alley behind his apartment. Selsam's prototypes can produce six times more power than a similarly sized single-rotor turbine. Doug is absolutely confident that they will scale up beautifully and be stable even in very strong winds.

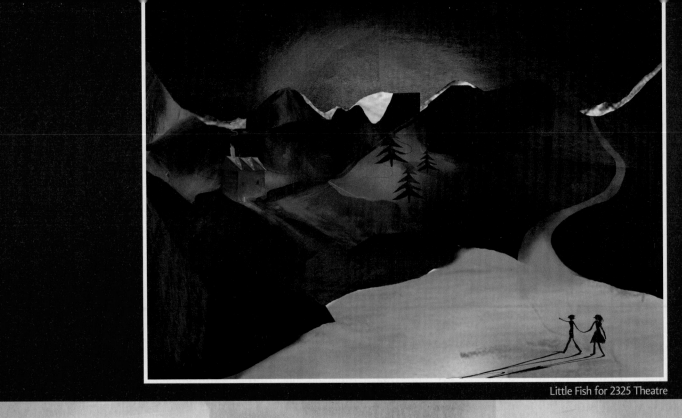
Little Fish for 2325 Theatre

Maud and Claude for Storyteller magazine

SOLAR DISCO TOWERS

THE POWER OF SUNSHINE hugely exceeds the global need for energy. Every hour the sun radiates more free energy than the entire human population uses in a year. Still, less than 1% of the energy used worldwide comes from solar power because we have yet to find a way to capture it cheaply and directly. By far the oldest method has been biomass: sunshine is captured by trees, for example and then the wood is burned. A more recent method collects concentrated sunshine with mirrors. Simply point the mirror at the sun and concentrate the energy onto a carrying medium which once heated can power a turbine. Always assuming that there is sunshine.

But mirrors are not the only way to concentrate light. The lens found in every eye and every camera bends light to focus, but this kind of lens is too bulky to be affordable. The French engineer, Augustin-Jean Fresnel is credited with a solution that could change all this – originally developed to use in lighthouses in the 1820's. The Fresnel lens is a set of concentric annular lenses engraved or moulded on to a flat piece of glass or plastic. A Utah based company called IAUS has developed a Fresnel lens solar concentrator that utilises an inexpensive thin film of plastic material, making its units very low maintenance and cheap to build in comparison to traditional solar reflector panels. Four circular lens are mounted on a tower which automatically tracks the sun, magnifying the rays onto molten salt which in turn powers a steam turbine. IAUS boast that the cost of energy produced from a whole farm of their solar discs will equal that produced by coal.

Approximately 20 towers producing roughly 1MW are currently being erected on land near the Great Basin Desert in Eastern California and another project in Texas is in the offing. There are high hopes for these strange four-eyed beasts. 1000 towers could be enough to provide power for 50,000 homes, but an even better plan might be to site clusters of these solar discs in disused urban settings; perfect micro-generation for baking desert citizens thirsty for air-conditioning.

Cape Town, South Africa

The life of freelance illustrator Katrin Coetzer is hardly your typical 9-5. "I work from home, and could technically flop out of bed and straight onto the workbench but I get 'dressed for work' nonetheless (I put an apron on). Helps me get into work mode." But the whistle doesn't blow at any set hour. "Yeah, I'm a night owl. Black sky; clean slate. I find daytime light and noises very distracting, so the day often ends well after midnight." Katrin lives in Capetown, South Africa, where she works from a room above the garage, a room with a fabulous view of Table Mountain... and a monkey-puzzle tree.

As a child she dreamt of becoming a game ranger, which might explain her stockpile of pre-90's National Geographic magazines. "I'm very inquisitive, always looking around. I spent school holidays on our farm in the bush in Botswana and that's where I've always felt most like myself. I guess you could say that I'm a bit of a nature freak." So when she came across this brief? "Illustration and sustainable design? My two favourite brain occupiers!" In a remarkable shower of mark making, Katrin's illustration describes light as energy translated into "idyllic nighttime energy consumption... because I'm a night owl I'm very dependent on light at night." For most of the year evenings in South Africa are warm, so people enjoy plenty of time outdoors. "Illustrating a night scene as well meant I could emphasise the electrical lights in contrast to the solar disc tower soaking up the sun's

rays in the daytime. I love the idea of guilt-free energy consumption, so I showed the outdoors and people at leisure." All that flat black background had Katrin reaching for her Plaka paints; "which create the flattest of flat colour, but not flat like Photoshop. I try to do as little as possible on the computer."

Katrin usually puts in a few hours tidying her studio before an afternoon stroll with a sketchbook for doodling. "I am very, very untidy." When in the throes of work she spreads things out. "Oh dear, it's chaotic, but it's the way I love it." Like tracking animal behaviour in the bush, she says you can tell when it's been a productive day by the abundance of empty coffee cups. Other requirements for

a good day's work include "my mobile phone, for the daily 'work well my love' text from my boyfriend, and music, although because it slices my attention in half I keep the volume down." The majority of Katrin's time is spent researching content and concepts. On her strolls through Capetown, Katrin snaps the faded lettering on the dilapidated facades of Art Deco buildings. "Then I juxtapose found images of the most divergent subjects I can find and force a relationship between them." She enjoys the ability of an illustration to help envision an abstract concept that is hard to verbalise.

How does she know when to put down the pencil? "It's never done. I need a deadline. Working for myself and on my own, I can feel isolated, but this is made easier when advice and knowledge are shared." Katrin is not afraid to solicit the help of friends in advertising and word of mouth recommendations, as well as seeking out interesting-looking open briefs on the internet. As for feedback, "It's important, but I try to filter it well. I only seek out the really harsh critics when I'm too tired to take the criticism personally. Generally though, I've learnt to be gentler with myself than in the past." At the moment Katrin is also cribbing up on her business skills, learning to be a silversmith, "the idea of being a jeweller is tempting but I'm definitely not skilled or speedy enough to make it lucrative", and is about to embark on a post grad in illustration. "I need to step up my juggling skills!"

Katrin worries about the changes occurring in the natural world but what really gives her concern are "the boundaries that nations have forced on the global physical environment. I'd like to think I could go where I want on a whim, but I can't because of the strange system that is border control." Despite its political struggles Katrin is incredibly proud of her breathtaking coastal city. "It's true, Capetonians often sound smug, but it can't be helped. We live nestled up against a jaw-dropping mountain in the Cape Floral Kingdom, surrounded on three sides by beaches." She's intrigued and inspired by the rough inner city zones of South Africa's big cities, acknowledging that they can be shocking to many visitors. "But there is a great deal of cross-cultural development and collaboration now which is very exciting."

She is a champion of the lowly earthworm. "Vermiculture! I mean why not? We all have vegetable waste, so why not turn it into amazing fertilizer as if by magic? I love watching worms turn waste into good compost." She grows her own veggies and plants indigenous 'water–wise' plants, particularly trees, which are "my new favourite wedding gift. I'm at that age where great hordes of my friends are getting hitched." South Africa's tree of the year in 2009 is a Monkey Thorn. "Hmm, that gives me an idea for a series of illustrations…"

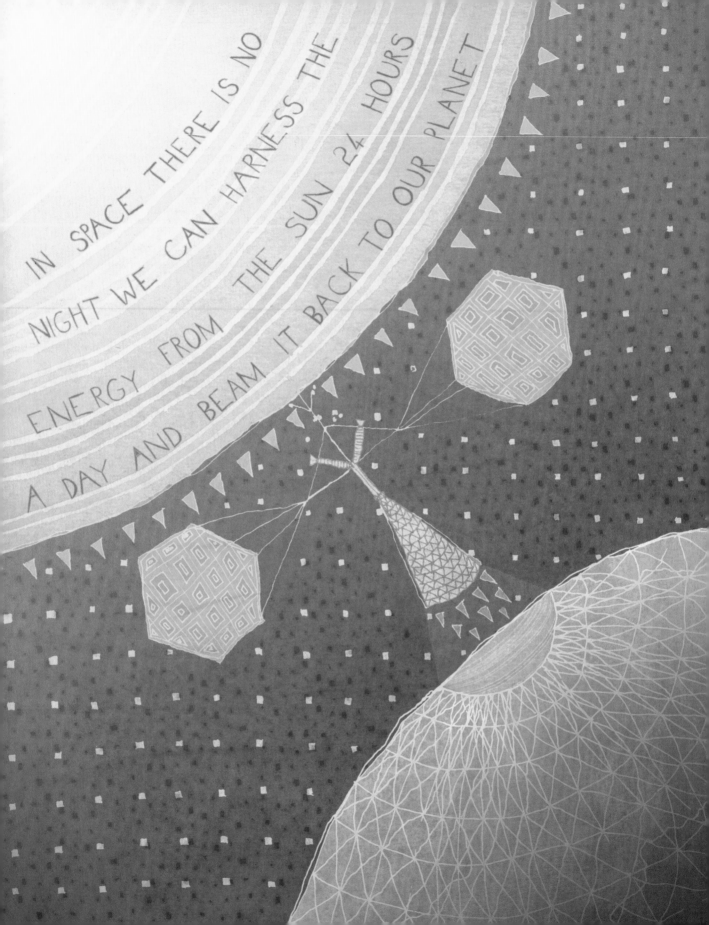

IN SPACE THERE IS NO NIGHT WE CAN HARNESS THE ENERGY FROM THE SUN 24 HOURS A DAY AND BEAM IT BACK TO OUR PLANET

ORBITAL SOLAR

The idea of creating a solar space farm has been popular since the heyday of space travel during the 60's, but possibly not for ecological reasons. It would be relatively simple to place a weapon on such a station, and doomsayers speak of 'death-rays' that could fry a whole city. Engineers working on the idea say that there is no chance whatsoever of the power-transfer beam misfiring and cooking a passing plane or a bit of city, but there are still questions to be answered about the effect that energy of approximately one-sixth the strength of noon sunlight will have on passing birds. Another frightening possibility might be the temptation to fix the climate a little – so for instance the beam could be directed onto oceans to stir up tropical storms and drive additional evaporation – with possibly diabolical consequences.

Despite these worries, companies in both the US and Japan have declared their intention to build and launch solar space stations within the next decade. The huge amount of power harvested from outer space will be beamed back to base stations on Earth in the form of electromagnetic waves, either as lasers or microwaves. The Japanese plan to put four square kilometres of solar photovoltaic panels into geostationary orbit above the Earth to test their beams and figure out the impact of the vast quantity of space debris on the solar farm. A pilot project should be in place by 2015, with the eventual means to produce 1GW of power, enough to provide for almost 300,000 homes.

In California a small company called Solaren is working with a big utility to get an orbiting solar station into space even faster. They rather ambitiously declare that, because the underlying technology (used in communications satellites) already exists, they could power up to half a million homes within the next ten years. To address issues of cost they will use pre-existing launch pads and vehicles to make only four or five trips into space to build this beast, using only low carbon fuels. While it is unlikely that a massive shaft of pure energy could be deployed for James Bond villain type destruction, it is true that the American government has recommended that the first systems be deployed to provide the military with power, because they alone can afford to pay the premium it would cost. Once in position they promise their station will have a zero carbon footprint. Time to dust off and reappraise those sci-fi fantasies?

THE BEST PLACE to capture solar energy is somewhere where there are no clouds and no atmospheric dust. Ever. And the sun shines 24 hours a day, 7 days a week, in huge quantities. A solar farm on the surface of the moon would do rather nicely, but there are a couple of small problems: how to build it and how to get the power to where it is needed.

A *slightly* less ambitious plan places a solar farm in orbit. The idea is science fiction. Literally. The science fiction author Isaac Asimov wrote a short story in 1941 that described a space station beaming microwave energy to a planet. Another science fiction author, Arthur C Clarke, proposed the idea of geostationary orbits (fixed in position above a certain point on earth) in 1945. A major barrier to this project is the cost of lifting stuff into space but good old Arthur had an answer for this too: a space elevator which rides up a 36,000km cable. Unfortunately the super-strong material needed for the cable has not yet been invented. But there may be another solution. Old-fashioned rockets use up most of their fuel lifting themselves, but what if a rocket could be lifted the first five kilometres on a giant kite? A wildly imaginative inventor has just applied for a patent to do exactly that: with a rocket-powered kite plane.

The sun and the moon work each day | to create our tides

offering a predictable and renewable

source of energy

solar panels on roof generate additional power

water squeezed through to increase pressure

blades divert flow onto turbine to generate power

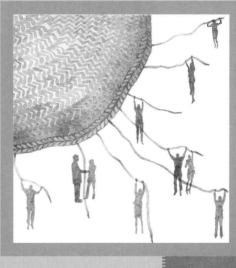

I'm a real geek about noise. I don't like the wrong kind of noise. I used to live in the centre of Reading and trucks would rush past and make the windows rattle. That drove me ballistic. Where I live now in Surrey it's really quiet and pretty, which means I can think straight.

I'm obsessed with Radio 4. The background noise keeps me company when I'm working but the problem is that I now only half know loads of really amazing and interesting things. So when I meet people I can never articulate myself very well.

I grew up in Wootton Bassett. No one knew where it was but it's become infamous as the place where soldiers pass through. My school has been knocked down and my family and friends have moved on so it's not really my hometown anymore. Now home is wherever my cats are; I'm a really creepy cat woman.

I did a fine art degree which involved endless criticism. It was buttock-clenchingly horrendous every time but now I find it really frustrating when someone says 'that's lovely' or 'that's nice, well done', because it gets you nowhere. My best critic is my partner Steve. He looks over my shoulder and is really honest so it's great to have him around to bounce ideas off, even if I usually hate him for about five minutes.

I've got the same laptop as James Bond. Just as I started my dissertation for my MA my old one stopped working and out of sympathy my parents bought the new one for me. I'm terrible with any kind of technology so when my dad turned up with it I just danced around the box, too scared to set it up. I've had it for four years now and it would break my heart if it broke.

I would love to be a hermit and spend all my time drawing. I'm obsessed with drawing by hand, but obviously if you create an illustration in blue and someone really wants it in green then you would be foolish not to take advantage of Photoshop. I'm getting really into handmade textures using paint washes that I scrub at with Brillo pads. I draw really slowly which is bad for commissions. I'll never be a computer girl but I do need it, especially for tight deadlines.

I get really cranky if I can't draw a lot. I use these pens that are really hard to get hold of and they break all the time. I love the process and physicality of producing a line, but I get annoyed because I feel as though I'm always trying to improve and I'm never pleased, which is a bit sad because when I look back I see that I am getting better. The pieces where I really mess up are the ones I learn the most from even though a bad drawing affects my life terribly. If I think about how much I still have to learn it's just horrendous but when something is going well I practically bounce off the walls.

My studio is really big and glorious but I've trashed it. Last year I did a screen-printing project for Christmas using some fluorescent turquoise emulsion and now it's stuck all over the carpet. I've also done a lot of spray painting and all the particles have settled so that if you move the furniture you can see that the whole carpet is now green. Last time – thanks to a genius carpet cleaner – we managed to get our deposit back even though our flat was a total mess, so hopefully that will work again.

I'm really ambitious in an obvious and naked way. But I'm not competitive. People relate success to money, nice clothes and holidays, yet you can be 'successful' and hate what you're doing. I feel content with my life just the way it is; in ten years time I hope it will be the same; with my family, which is Steve and my cats.

At first I wasn't going to do this brief because it involves science. At school I shut myself off from maths and science. I just wouldn't listen. But recently I've been getting more interested and I want to know how everything works. Because I was illustrating a technology

Kerry Lemon

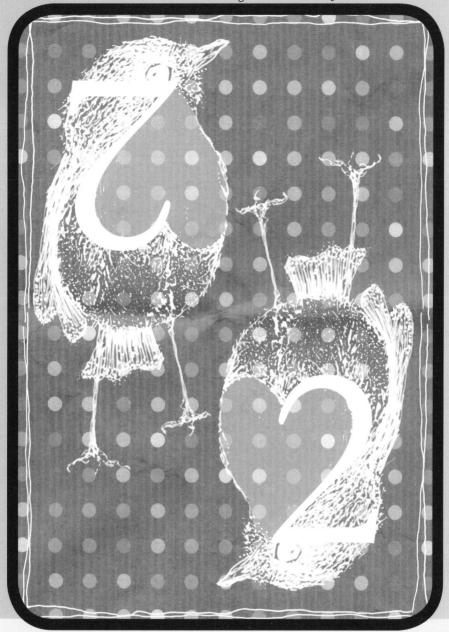

that doesn't yet exist I had to try and understand the science behind it, but there was nothing to inspire me until I read about there being no night time in space and then I clicked with the subject straight away. I find that a good way to understand high-brow ideas is through kids' books and TV, especially the news for kids. It's exciting to get my head around a complex concept and once I get going I find it hard to stop.

Science and art share a lot of common ground. Doing this brief made me think a lot about collaboration between the two because I personally find climate change hard to relate to, especially that whole 'polar bear on an ice cube' thing. When I think about the whole concept I feel frozen into inaction, but with this brief I feel that in a small way I can contribute something useful. No one solution will be enough to solve climate change but we can combine knowledge and effort to make a difference.

HOT ROCK
TECHNOLOGY

FLATS

HOT ROCK TECHNOLOGY

THE VERY **CENTRE OF THE EARTH** is hotter than the surface of the sun, so it stands to reason that there is more geothermal energy right under our feet than we could ever need. Where the surface of the planet is cracked this heat is forced up to create volcanoes and boiling springs, making it easy to extract geothermal power. All over the world, from Iceland to the Phillippines, geysers are enjoyed as recreational spas as well as being used to heat homes and generate power. Today the largest geothermal power plant is in California at the aptly named patch of wooded hills called The Geysers, where a host of power plants produces enough electricity for over a million people.

But imagine if you could tap geothermal power from everywhere, not just those places where it most obviously rises to the top. In principle all that is needed is to drill a few holes several kilometres down into the earth, then pump cold water deep down into the 'hot rocks' and pull boiling water and steam back up to power some turbines; once it has cooled down, the cycle continues. Enhanced Geothermal, (otherwise known as Hot Rock Technology) sounds so simple on paper.

But it isn't. Over the past 35 years more than 600 million dollars worldwide has been spent trying to figure out how all this heat can be successfully accessed. The trick is in finding the right kind of rocks; relatively close to the surface, fractured or able to fracture horizontally, and not in a critically dangerous earthquake zone. And it takes a mammoth amount of money to drill down so far into the earth, so if an estimation is wrong a lot of money goes to waste. The problems are multiple, and despite a lot of excitement from geophysical engineers an awful lot has been going wrong lately.

In 2006 a massive earthquake in Basel, Switzerland called a dramatic halt to a geothermal pilot plant being built (rather strangely) on a significant fault line, one that had managed to completely flatten the town in 1356. The earthquakes, including four above magnitude 3, rattled on for about a year – more than 3,500 in all. Proponents of geothermal energy point out that stations should be kept away from large urban areas but despite this, in 2009 two other projects saw major setbacks. AltaRock in the US, partly funded by Google, was first to falter. The official line is that drilling in The Geysers had discovered 'geologic anomalies' but residents are increasingly worried about its proximity to two large fault lines, not to mention the city of San Francisco. Current geothermal plants in the area have already adversely affected the number of minor earthquakes. It seems like common sense. Blasting deep rock into smithereens near a fault line is foolhardy at best – for we don't really know how fractures are connected together miles below the earth. In the Cooper Basin area of Australia a similar project has met with an uncontrolled release of steam and hot water at the wellhead. It took the operators a month to get the well back under control with weighted mud, and the well was then capped with two cement plugs.

But there is hope on the horizon – a small 1.5MW test plant at Soultz-Sous-Forêts in France has been running since 2008, thus far without problems; there are plans afoot to extend this facility to provide 20MW of power. And in Cornwall, UK planning permission has been applied for, to drill a pair of boreholes into the granite outcrops directly beneath the visionary Eden Project centre. And if all these grand plans come to nothing there is always geothermal heat pumps, which can be installed almost anywhere to provide central heating or air conditioning by pumping heat to or from the ground, where the ambient temperature remains higher than the surrounding air even just below the surface. A far simpler and relatively low tech solution, and proven to work in thousands of homes already.

WHEN LAURA BIRD was a child she wanted to work with animals. One of her first drawings was a Save the Whales poster which was displayed in her local shop. Now she obsesses over ancient artefacts whilst considering ways in which her work as an illustrator can inspire change.

Describe a typical day of work for you.

I usually start off by making lists and generally getting myself organised, which can take a while. I do 'serious' work from mid afternoon into the evening and if I'm really into a project I'll stay up most of the night working on it. Working from home means I'm in control of my own schedule, and I fear that I'm slowly becoming more and more nocturnal.

What does your work space look like at the moment?

Since graduating from uni I've been living at home in Wales and have converted my parent's conservatory into a makeshift studio. It's great because I can see into the garden and forest behind the house. My working environment could be described as a mess, but I know where everything is and if anything gets tidied up or moved I usually get annoyed. I'm not even surrounded by things which inspire me, I'm just messy; my problem is that I never throw anything away. I use quite a bit of collage in my work so there are always tiny scraps of paper floating around that I keep in case I need them later on, and my sculptures are dotted all over the house which isn't ideal. But I'm going to be moving into a studio in East London with the This Is It collective soon.

How did This Is It come together?

I have only just graduated so I am still very much in touch with the people I met at uni; not just illustrators but fine artists, animators, film makers and writers – being able to get their opinions is a great advantage because it makes me consider things I would never have thought of by myself. The other ten members of This Is It all went to Kingston University too. It is very important to me to work collaboratively so we plan to work on group drawings and exhibitions together.

Do you look to other illustrators for inspiration?

I try not to look at the work of other illustrators because I usually feel bad about my own when I see how good they are, and I don't want to be influenced by whatever is the latest trend. I find it much more productive to find inspiration in other art forms so I often research ideas from African, Mexican, Aztec and Native American art and textiles. I really like sculpture so I love going to the British Museum to look at the ancient art, especially the masks. I admire the skill that was needed to produce such great characters and the colours are often wonderful.

How would you describe your process?

I try to experiment with as many different processes as I can; paint, ink, crayons, pencil, print, collage and found objects. I like things that look handmade, and I use quite a lot of sculpture in my work. I don't think that I have a set style or particular process of working, as it changes quite a lot depending on what I feel like creating that day. My sketchbooks contain workings out and lists so they don't really make a lot of sense. I am very jealous of artists who create beautiful sketchbooks filled with delicate things. One day I really want to make a sketchbook like that.

What intrigued you about this project?

I thought the brief was interesting because there was plenty to explore and I specifically wanted to work on something that I had never heard of before. I was intrigued by the name, Hot Rock technology, so I read a few articles and began to get ideas together that would convey the principles in a playful rather than technical way, to make it look exciting and interest people in learning more. Working on this project has made me realise just how many alternative energy sources there are out there, and how many more we haven't even discovered yet. This year I also produced illustrations for the Biomimicry talk at the Greengaged design conference, on ways in which design can work with nature to improve our environment. I met so many interesting people who made me realise that it's not just up to scientists, architects and engineers to consider environmental issues in their work. As an illustrator I also have a responsibility to spread the message of a need for change in the way we live. Sustainability is something that anyone and everyone should get involved with.

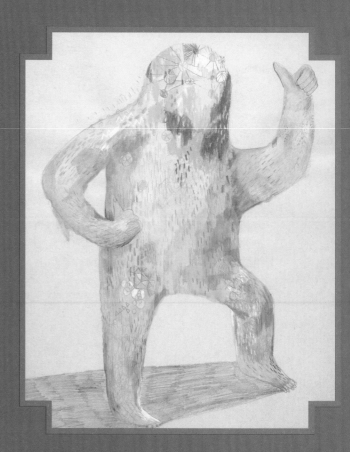

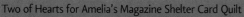

Two of Hearts for Amelia's Magazine Shelter Card Quilt

A.

RBS
The Royal Bank of ~~Scotland~~
Sustainability

Royal Bank of Sustainability for Amelia's Magazine
and Platform at C Words, Arnolfini

THE FIRST HYDROGEN FUEL CELL was invented nearly 200 years ago by Swansea based scientist Sir William Robert Grove, but has yet to become a commercially viable technology. Hydrogen fuel cells generate electrical power quietly and efficiently without pollution (the byproduct is simply water) using only a supply of hydrogen and oxygen. The technology has long been proposed as a pollution-free power source for vehicles and for microgeneration units in buildings. So what's the problem? Although oxygen is abundant and everywhere around us, free hydrogen does not occur naturally, and must be manufactured. It is also a highly volatile and combustible gas that is difficult to handle and store.

And so the race is on to find a cheap way of producing hydrogen. Even though it can be powered by electricity from a multitude of renewable sources (for example, wind-turbines), electrolysis of water to split it into hydrogen and oxygen is still inefficient and expensive. For this reason most hydrogen is produced from natural gas, oil and coal, all of which produce that most unfortunate of byproducts: carbon dioxide.

There is a glimmer of hope that the whacky hypothesis espoused by the Russian geologist Vladmir Larin could turn out to be true. His Hydridic Earth theory proposes that the middle and lower mantles of the earth are composed almost entirely of hydrides. Whilst remaining completely unproved, this could explain the presence of hydrogen vents on the ocean floor and would have profound implications for energy production if we ever learnt how to drill deep enough to exploit the hydrogen inside the earth.

Another idea that seems more feasible exploits the growth of a certain type of algae in anaerobic conditions (without oxygen). In 1939 a German researcher named Hans Gaffron observed that the algae *Chlamydomonas reinhardtii* would sometimes switch from the production of oxygen to the production of hydrogen. Unfortunately he never discovered the cause of this change and it was not until the late 1990's that professor Anastasios Melis at the University of California discovered that if the algae culture medium is deprived of sulphur it will produce hydrogen for a few days before returning to normal processes. So far algae has not been persuaded to produce hydrogen continuously with satisfactory efficiency, but trials continue in several universities. If a practical method is found, algae could be the ideal carbon-free supplier of hydrogen for fuel cells.

LAURA ALICE THOMPSON is an illustrator and textile designer based in Bradford, England. As a child her favourite book was Eric Carle's The Hungry Caterpillar and she's inspired by the contrasting colours in nature, the organic formations of fungi... and patterns made by crochet. Whilst studying for an MA in Textile Design in Sweden Laura fell in love with illustration. She also produces textile jewellery and bespoke wall hangings.

She gets about a bit...

I did work experience in Sweden before returning to work at a fashion print agency in London for a while, then I decided to concentrate on my own business. The owner of Magic Number Three – a local shop that stocks the work of ethical designers – has been a brilliant help in learning how to go it alone. I use blogs and Twitter to communicate with people and I regularly check the Amelia's Magazine website because I've just started to enter competitions, although this is the first I've been successful with! I'm a member of a few artists' networks, including ArtHouse in Wakefield, and they send out bulletins about upcoming competitions and events so I try to enter as many as I can. I like living in the North because it's easier to approach people and get your work out there. London scares me!

She's always been crafty...

I had a very vivid imagination as a child and always loved drawing stories and creating fantasy worlds. My sister was a fantastic artist so I was fascinated by her expression and style and I used to collect lots of arty postcards and graphics posters. Most of my work is brightly coloured – it's what I see first, so I use it to draw the viewer in – and highly patterned. I try to be refreshing and positive in the way I design. The ArtHouse helped me to set up my business by providing a studio and free courses and at first it was great to be around other artists, but now I'm a bit more established it's easier and cheaper to work at home in the studio attic that I share with my husband Danny, who produces music.

She's no stranger to sustainability...

I did a lot of research on sustainable technologies during my masters, which focused on the philosophy of long-term design and ways in which to design a product to give it more value and meaning to the user so that they treasure it more

deeply and are therefore less likely to throw it away. I enjoy the process of mixing science and creativity and felt inspired by this brief to delve in once again because I like learning about how things work and channeling that into illustration, which is definitely a challenge since most of my work is abstract or fashion based.

She has got a bit of a thing for algae...

I first heard about the hydrogen fuel cell at a symposium in Sweden called Design for Prosperity and thought it seemed like an under-developed area compared to wind and solar power, then I found that algae could produce hydrogen in certain conditions and thought this was a brilliant solution. Plus I was really inspired by the beautiful magnified pictures of algae because I love weird organic forms and the way things in nature repeat slightly differently. So I decided to make the algae exaggerated and playful with bright luminous colours and lots of pattern to emphasise life and movement. There are so many solutions out there, you just have to dig deep.

She advocates the power of community...

I think that most of our problems are intrinsic to society and need to be addressed in the longterm through education. I think that the reduce, re-use and recycle concept is a positive and accessible solution that should be promoted as much as possible, as well as using alternative modes of transport. Community activities to boost morale can be a massive help but if I could change one thing today I think I would make people more considerate so we could all be happier. I hope in the future that we will have found and adopted lots of creative solutions to climate change and the way we live.

She's a responsible lady...

I try to be eco-conscious and am particularly careful about what I consume, so instead of buying heaps of rubbish at Primark I like to invest in remade clothes and fashions. My view is that all design should take ethical considerations into account, so I use reclaimed fabrics and yarns in my textiles. Designers and creatives have huge influence so we can make a big difference. I've applied to do further research in environmental design because I believe it is such an extremely important area to work on and I'm also developing ideas for large-scale art projects to educate children about climate change at a local level.

LEONA CLARKE studied graphic design at Chelsea College of Art and Design. "At the end of the course my lecturer told me I should go and do illustration." So now she draws and designs online games "anything from bingo to social networking" for a company during the day and pursues her love of illustration during the evenings and weekend. "So I suppose it's a bit like having two jobs!" She would love to be a full-time illustrator, but concedes that due to time constraints she doesn't spend as much time as she should looking for freelance work. "On the upside I've gained a lot of technical knowledge from my job – one day I'd like to design my own product range, but at the moment I feel as though I've got the best of both worlds."

She's a self-confessed girlie girl. "I like to draw pretty things. I'm inspired by the feminine illustrative style of the 60's and 70's when everyone had such huge eyes. I always give my characters big eyes." She enjoyed the recent exhibition showcasing the work of Alan Aldridge. "My favourite part was the green mirrored room featuring huge cutouts of creatures from his book The Butterfly Ball and the Grasshopper's Feast. It was great to see his use of colour and gradients in so much detail." She has a big desk in the corner of her living room, that is usually covered in books. "I've got lots of Art Deco and Art Nouveau Dover design books and I collect fashion magazines." One of her favourite books is full of traditional Japanese textile designs, known as Wasarasa patterns. "I always look at that one. I first discovered it in the library at college and I kept it out on loan for a whole year. It's out of print but fortunately I was given an old copy as a gift." She uses a mix of hand drawing and computers to achieve a polished result, "I normally sketch out my ideas but then I'll use Illustrator or Photoshop to redraw them and colour them in. I often prefer the results that are possible with a computer."

Leona checks out the blogosphere on a regular basis. "I upload my work to Flickr and I like to see what other people are doing so I follow over fifty blogs in my news feed, everything from interiors to music and art. I find blogs are like a daisy chain; I go from one to another by looking at which blogs my favourite bloggers are reading." She is a fan of online competitions. "Illustration Friday is a great website that comes up with a different word to submit a drawing for each week." Leona did an amusing interpretation of sustainability for an illustration of the word 100%. " I drew a girl knitting a jumper and the words '100% Wool' straight from a lamb." She tries to leave a comment below work that she likes because it's encouraging when she is on the receiving end. "I enjoy working to a brief, it's challenging at first but I like to have a concept to work with because it gives a better result than unplanned drawing." Even though Leona works alone on her illustrations, she finds it useful to seek advice from her boyfriend. "He trained as a designer so he has a good creative mind. Friends at work are also good to bounce ideas off." She doesn't mind the odd bit of rejection. "During my first year at university I had a really tough tutor so I'm used to getting the kind of criticism that helps produce a better result."

She has had to educate herself for several climate change related projects. Working with Amelia she designed the poster for Climate Camp 2008, and found it deeply satisfying to see it flyposted up around London. "It's enjoyable to learn about sustainable issues and it tends to affect my everyday life at the same time as meeting a brief." This was followed by a commission from EcoLabs to depict the dire consequences of six degrees global warming based on a chapter in a book by Mark Lynas. "I had to read the whole of Six Degrees to do that project and I learned a lot of thoroughly depressing and scary stuff about climate change. I didn't realise that we could expect six degrees of warming so soon, and just how much damage this would cause." She based the image on a famous painting by the French Romantic painter Théodore Géricault called The Raft of the Medusa. "People would be forced to risk their lives and take to the sea in search of somewhere to live because there would be no other option." In the background an ark offers hope as the sun blazes down across the devastated landscape. She prefers to cycle everywhere now. "I stopped driving a few years ago because I don't really need a car – if I do I can always use Streetcar, which is much more sustainable because lots of people share one vehicle."

As for the Deep Green Kite power system that Leona chose to illustrate, she was attracted to the idea of illustrating the sea. She also had a go at illustrating the BioStream technology. "I liked the way that the technology is modelled on a tail fin of a fish." She based her depiction on the colourful montages used in album cover art from the 60's. "I wanted to show how the technology could be used to power a multitude of electronic devices. Cooking is integral to our lives and it brings people together, as do music and festivals. I included my computer because it allows me to create and communicate." The resulting image may not be entirely accurate in showing such direct delivery of the energy, but as with all of Leona's work it is of course beautifully stylish and engaging.

Six Degrees, Future Scenarios
for EcoLabs Climate Roadshow

London Smiles When the Sun Comes Out, Know Magazine

London Needs You!

...help decide your city of the future

Come join us in the London neighbourhood at **Climate Camp**
for a week of sustainable living, workshops, debates, direct action and fun

London neighbourhood poster for Climate Camp at Kingsnorth, Kent in 2008

*S*ince the 1980's the Canadian (and sometime jeweller) Philippe Vauthier has been designing a machine that makes use of underwater currents. Named the Underwater Electric Kite, his turbines rise and fall in search of the layer of water that runs fastest, much as a kite does, on gusts of wind. Meanwhile the researchers at Strathclyde University in Scotland are seeking funding for a turbine that sounds remarkably similar. Cormat is moored rather than fixed to the seabed so that it can move with the flow of the tides.

The Deep Green giant underwater turbine goes one better. Developed by the Swedish firm Minesto, it not only seeks to capture the power of the ocean just like a kite in the wind, but it is shaped and moves like one. And funnily enough the idea springs from a concept designed to take advantage of the wind, which was reworked when it was realised that it could work better in the water, which is 800 denser than air. The giant 7 tonne kite has a 12m wingspan that twirls in a figure of eight pattern; when the force of the waves hits it the device turns down, which creates a lift force to power the turbines. It is claimed that this method increases the velocity entering the turbines by ten times the actual flow speed, so that each unit can generate 500KW. Moored to the seabed at a depth of 60-150m with a tether that transmits the electricity to shore, the rudder is computer-controlled to follow the desired trajectory.

A first prototype confirmed that this technology works and is capable of producing far more electricity for far less infrastructure than larger turbines. Having received some help from the UK government, Minesto is now headquartered in Belfast, Northern Ireland, from which a larger sea-worthy prototype will very shortly be launched .

Deep Green Kite

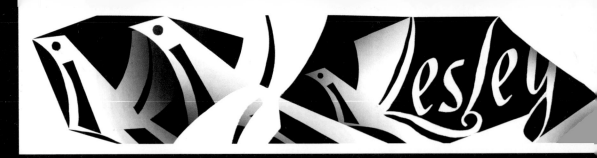

ESLEY BARNES has a bit of a thing for books. "When I'm putting together an image I imagine that I'm designing a book cover," she explains. By her own admission the best thing about her childhood was all the books she read. "I wanted to make the monsters in Where the Wild Things Are real!" Monsters have been a recurring theme in her work, noticeably in her short animation Herzog and Monsters, which won a stream of awards and has been shown all over the world. "I went to a screening in Bradford... but the best one was at Chicago International Children's Film Festival. They paid for me to go out there for a week, and I got to meet loads of other animators that I'm still in touch with." In this charming film a boy is forbidden from reading the books that fill his grandmother's house; he retreats into his own world, creating monster tales of his own with cut up letters. It's not hard to see where Lesley's inspiration has come from. "When I was a child I remember loving the way that letters were visually made part of the story in picture books."

During her teenage years Lesley discovered Saul Bass, who created title sequences for Hitchcock films such as Vertigo. "I like the way a good opening can capture the narrative and build excitement without giving anything of the story away." She was to use this technique when working on Haunted Hogmanay for BBC Scotland. "I used stop motion to create spooky scenes from the Old Town." She constructed Edinburgh out of photocopies. "They create a great texture. I used the photocopier so much at art college that I was banned from using it."

It took awhile for Lesley to realise her calling – in fact her love of reading led her to first complete a degree in English Literature before moving on to work with images after she did an internship in the submissions department at the Edinburgh Film Festival and realised that the only films she wanted to take home were the animations. "I think I'm quite lucky," she says, somewhat self-deprecatingly. "I was never a great writer. But they needed people on the MA in Motion Graphics [at Glasgow School of Art] so I showed them some stuff that I had done at home and I got a place."

She now works from her parent's house, where she has taken over the attic. "I persuaded them to clear out the junk room next to my bedroom. I've got a big 'partners desk' with three computers

on it in the middle of the room, and I'm surrounded by books and piles of papers. It's quite messy really." She also keeps lots of screen prints and photos around as inspiration, and occasionally watches films on her computer when she should be working. A favourite is the work of animator Lotte Reiniger, who worked with stylised silhouette cut-outs during the first part of the 20th century. "It can be a bit lonely," she admits, but bonuses include: multiple cups of tea (strong with just a bit of milk) delivered by her mum, and tales of treefrogs and crabs from her zoologist dad. Plus she has just joined the Gin Palace collective, a group of designers from different disciplines, and they plan to exhibit together. The best thing about living in Scotland is "mountains, rain and Tunnock's tea cakes." But London sounds quite exciting, and Lesley is beginning to feel an inexorable pull.

Most of Lesley's work comes via her London-based agency (who find advertising jobs), from contacts at film festivals, or from people who have found her on the internet – as was the case with Matt Saunders,

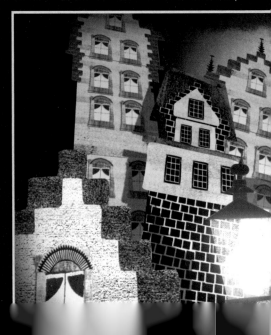

who she describes as her "email friend." He lives in Leeds and they've never actually met but they are working collaboratively on a documentary about disruptive children. "We're attempting to animate their quite random drawings of space rockets." Matt has been working on the stop motion side of things whilst Lesley concentrates on the type and drawings; "it's a combination of our styles." She hopes they will meet in real life sometime soon.

Lesley couldn't live without black Indian ink and big sheets of blank paper, on which she creates shapes to scan into Photoshop, where she moves things around and adds the occasional bit of colour. It was something of a challenge to work with so many colours on the endpapers for the Anthology, "It was really nice though, I think I might start using more colours." The idea of solar ink appealed to her because "the sun is responsible for everything isn't it? Even the wind and the tides... I was reminded of a quote about the world not being short of energy, but merely short of ways to capture it." She would

have liked to create the illustration using some ac "But I guess that would be a bit of a waste since it's i of a dark sunless book!" Instead her illustration dep erful sun painting rolls of paper with words in solar positive about the future. Even someone like me is v until a few years ago didn't think much about the env best thing that could happen would be if everyone st issues seriously, but she worries that people get to their own lives. "And there's too many cheap things stuff. We need to cut that down."

Oxfam bookshops provide a fertile hunting g Penguins on which Lesley spends "quite a lot of m sometimes reads. Agatha Christie novels always g "They were amongst the first 'adult' books that I way there was always a clever twist at the end." Les read a good thriller in bed and has just finished The S Whicher by Kate Summerscale and Arthur & George She can bookmark these with her "magical creature by night" – beautiful printed leather bookmarks wh Etsy and in gift shops. "They go all soft and last forev really nice presents."

Lesley's website boasts random phrases tha things she likes. Perhaps it's time to delve into he has something of a penchant for burnt toast and i food in general. "I like all that burnt stuff on the not supposed to be very good for you is it?" She lik dressed businessmen wearing red socks, and is pa pair herself. "It's really nice to be able to look at yo cheered up if you're having a bad day." She is ena cassette tapes that she made as a child, featuring off the radio and made up stories. Jack Nicholson has the most cunning smile of anyone she can think a special feature, not many people have a good cu Lesley's swag bag we would find "lots of shiny brass keys that look like they would open really big door bury some treasure she'd do it at the end of her "otherwise I wouldn't remember where it was." Oh definitely has the best selection of 'old lady' hats.

logos for Green Kite Midnight, Amelia's ceilidh band

Royal Bank of Sustainability for Amelia's Magazine
and Platform at C Words, Arnolfini

Two of Hearts for Amelia's Magazine Shelter Card Quilt

Solar ink

Several companies around the world are frantically experimenting with the production of super light-weight and flexible solar ink by nanoengineering particles at an atomic scale – creating functioning photovoltaic systems which require far less silicon than conventional ones, thereby depleting less resources. Innovalight, based in California, is experimenting with the liquification of cheap, unpurified silicon nanocrystals – that's an extremely fine powder to you and me, each particle being 10,000 thinner than a strand of human hair – that can be printed onto almost any surface using a simple inkjet printer. They do this by blasting silicon molecules with a 'radiofrequency plasma' so that they can be coerced into different positions and then suspended in a solvent. The whole substance is then poured onto whatever is the substrate and the excess liquid is drained off to leave a crystalline silicon structure. In 2009 it was announced that Innovalight had achieved an 18% efficiency in converting light to electricity, a record amongst purveyors of solar inks. Their hope is that they can push this up to over 20%. Solar ink in this form could be used to cover almost anything, from clothing and vehicles to roof tiles and even windows.

Of course, it's never quite that simple. Solar ink or paint or spray would still need to be applied carefully and evenly to surfaces at the right angle to receive maximum sunlight. There is no telling how long it would last; solar panels that are protected by glass from the elements have a life span of 25 years or more, but paint, as most homeowners are only too aware, doesn't always weather quite so well. And how would your freshly solar ink-washed wall be hooked into the electric grid? All these things still need to be answered.

Additionally, the vast majority of companies exploring nanotechnology are 'cleantech' companies aligned to the high-tech boom that began in Silicon Valley in the San Francisco Bay Area during the 1980's. When the self-professed desire is to make a lot of money (over and above protecting the environment) any success will have to be weighed against the perils of perpetuating our current capitalist system.

Solar ink can

be printed cheaply

Solar ink

onto

light flexible Sheets

ink Solar

POO POWER

Animal waste – our waste – produces a biogas cocktail as it breaks down. During a process called anaerobic digestion, biodegradable matter ferments to produce various gases, including methane, a greenhouse gas that is over twenty times more potent than carbon dioxide. We can avoid producing this methane if human waste, agricultural waste, waste paper and any kind of organic waste stays out of landfill and is instead turned into biogas, which can then be used to power Combined Heat and Power plants. Yes, poo power really could solve all our problems in one fell swoop.

The idea has been around for a long time. In 1859 an anaerobic digester was built to power a leper colony in India and in 1895 a septic tank was used to generate gas for street lights in Exeter, UK. Small biogas plants are gaining popularity all over the world, particularly in rural areas of India and China, where proximity to animals can easily provide cheap energy for cooking and lighting. In a typical Indian biodigester, animal (and human) dung and plant waste is mixed with water and passed into a digesting tank where it ferments. Apart from cutting down methane there are other benefits. The gas produced can be used for cooking, which greatly reduces the mainly female drudgery of collecting firewood and tending a fire. Fewer trees are cut down. The health risks from dirty smoke are reduced. The only waste material is a top quality compost with a high nitrogen content that can be used in place of fossil fuel derived chemical fertilisers.

We are unlikely to be able to meet all our power needs from human poop alone, but we desperately need to control the methane that is produced by animals farmed for meat. Of course we should just stop eating so much meat, but a second best short-term solution would be to take advantage of animal excrement to generate electricity. From a dog waste disposal scheme in the San Francisco Bay Area to biogas-run buses and trains in Sweden, poo power offers a viable way to generate renewable energy all over the world. Repeat after me: less waste equals more power.

LETITIA BUCHAN would be the first to admit that she has taken a circuitous route to illustration. Having travelled around the world several times she has finally settled down in Melbourne, where she works as a graphic and textiles designer for a large clothing brand. "I am mostly self taught in illustration and design; getting a job has been a question of being in the right place at the right time." This brief offered her an opportunity to do something fun and interesting with a topic that she wouldn't normally work on. "At work I have to bear in mind fashion trends, so my illustrations don't develop organically. I try to keep my own illustrations much less commercial by using a lot of hand drawn typography and textures."

Some of her predominant influences have come about as a result of her extensive travel. "I spent five years in South Africa and travelled in Zimbabwe, Botswana, Namibia, Mozambique and Swaziland so I have seen a lot of African culture." She lived in a tiny town on the borders of Kruger National Park, and speaks with fondness of the monkeys, resident wild hippo and snakes. "It was a breathtaking place to live and I drew animals most days. I had a more realistic style back then, but I love the way the animals still turn up in my work." She was especially inspired by the colourful geometric patterns of the Ndebele peoples' homes and clothing, and speaks with admiration of the bold Pop Art-esque West African wax print fabrics that feature images telling a story about the wearer. "I like the fact that the clothing has more significance than pure surface decoration. Overall it is the spirit of African people that has left the biggest imprint on me."

From rural Africa Letitia moved to London, and carried on travelling through Turkey, Spain, Italy, France, Morocco, Egypt, India, Japan, Sweden and Finland. One of her most memorable experiences was working aboard the superyacht of the Qatar Royal Family, which she thoroughly enjoyed. Alone on night duty she would play Lamb as loudly as she could in her sound-proofed room. "I drew all night long, stopping only when I was called for something, usually pistachio ice-cream at 5am in the morning!" Nowadays she harbours a dream of living in Amsterdam, where she would cycle along the pretty canals to work in a little design studio, but for now Melbourne is home and she concedes that as a veritable melting pot of cultures it is a great place to live.

Through connections to the mixed media Arterial Collective, Leititia is involved in a project to put together a series of artworks that will be shown in both Melbourne and Barcelona. "It's so that artist communities can establish a dialogue to reflect on identity and strengthen relations." She occasionally teaches illustration and was recently honoured to judge a student exhibition. Plans for the future include the launch of her own stationery and homeware line: "I want to create beautiful things to share with others, but I'm going to start at a teeny tiny manageable level."

Letitia recommends becoming a member of Illustrators Australia, (only if you live in Australia, of course) because their website provides good exposure and a network of contacts for work opportunities. Her favourite online resource is the blog Design Sponge. "I must confess to following Once Wed too, initially because I was hunting out inspiration for a non-traditional rustic wedding, but now I'm addicted to all the beautiful wedding photography and graphic design. It makes me want to be a photographer and florist too." She is especially intrigued by various forms of typography and quirky colour palettes. "Rather than sketching, I tend to write down my feelings for certain objects and places and I take a lot of photos – there is so much going on everywhere, you only have to look." She hunts out lettering on posters, food packaging, old buildings and signs. "I'm really pro happy colours at the moment. Bright pink, red, yellow..." She keeps the work of Dutch artist Angelique Houtkamp on her walls for inspiration and other influences include Californian artist Tim Biskup, English animator Julia Pott, fellow Melbourne designer Beci Orpin, Russian typographer Fiodor Sumkin and the surrealist scribbler Justin Lee Williams.

How did she decide which technology to illustrate? "My fiancé gave me the poo idea. It's his favourite subject – his company designs mechanical equipment for the pre-treatment of waste water, so I've seen plenty of disgusting video footage that he's brought back from work." She discovered loads of amazing facts during her research into renewable technologies and became fascinated with Tree Bogs, a form of composting outdoor toilet surrounded by nutrient-hungry plants that quickly decompose human waste. "If I didn't live in the city I would have no problem sacrificing my own indoor toilet in favour of a Tree Bog."

She is also helping out with the publicity design for the Camp for Climate Action in Western Australia, which is targeting coal production in Collie. "The community will come together to take grassroots direct action to stop our dependence on coal for energy production and economic gain." Unfortunately Melbourne is a long way away so she won't be able to make the camp herself, but like most Australians Letitia is directly aware of the effects of rapid climate change – severe drought and bush fires are dealt with on an everyday basis – and tries to limit her water usage as much as possible. "It absolutely creates an awareness of the dramatic effects caused by climate change." She recycles extensively and rides a little black bicycle, named Boris – "I name everything" – instead of driving. Electricity usage in the Buchan house is kept to an absolute minimum.

When it comes to the individual impact of greenhouse gases methane is more harmful as it traps 21 times more heat than carbon dioxide.

WATER TREATMENT PLANT

process

CH4 is released during waste treatment process

Methane is cleaned in scrubbing towers & fed into engines

sewerage & industrial waste is pumped into the treatment plant

methane converts Clean Renewable Electricity

The heat trapped in the atmosphere by greenhouse gases like carbon dioxide and METHANE is a major impact towards global warming.

Instead of the methane being released into the atmosphere as a gas, treatment plants are able to transform it into a valuable resource.

The WIND that blew Benjamin Franklin's

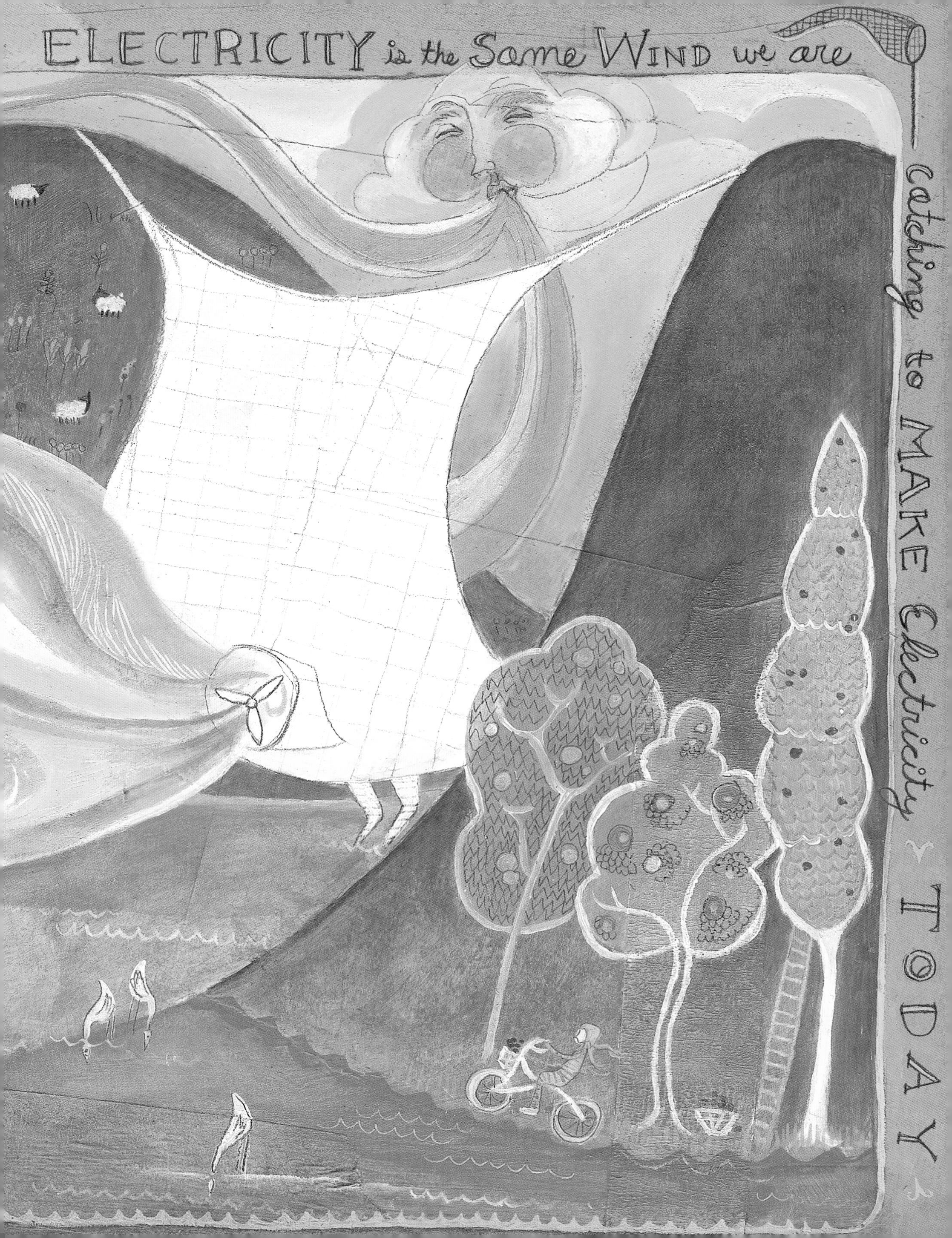
ELECTRICITY is the Same WIND we are
catching to MAKE Electricity TODAY

WIND DAM

SINCE THE 1880'S we've been generating hydroelectric power by placing huge concrete dams across rivers, not a particularly good idea for the environment it now turns out, but what if we could instead dam the wind? In broad terms the idea is similar: find a valley that funnels a strong prevailing wind and channel the wind through a turbine. Many inventors have thought about this, usually suggesting some sort of fence across the valley. For example, Charles Fry of Colorado filed a patent in 1978 proposing a cable stretched high across a valley from which hang shafts that carry vertical axis wind turbines. In more recent times Green Zephyr of New Zealand have proposed a stacked wall of turbines that look a bit like the cells of a beehive.

In 2007 UK-based architect Laurie Chetwood was inspired by the wind-capturing abilities of the spinnaker sails on yachts to invent a new kind of wind dam. Looking more like a Christo art installation than a power station, this gigantic kevlar sail would be supported on aluminium legs and strung across a mountain gorge above Lake Ladoga in Russia, where it would funnel winds into a central turbine enclosed in a tube. Interestingly, in the years since this was proposed, the Land Art Generator Initiative has been launched as a platform to encourage large scale artworks that can also generate power.

In all likelihood this dam would need significant alterations to make it viable. Queries have been raised as to how it could cope with concentrating dispersed turbulence, not to mention what might happen to any unfortunate birds that end up pinned helplessly to the giant sail. Kevlar sails degrade quickly in UV light and are notoriously difficult to clean, yet the idea has potential, especially for use in urban situations where it would likely be less intrusive and detrimental to the local environment. Imagine a huge sail strung across a bridge or between the towering wind tunnels that are created by skyscrapers...

All these ideas pale beside the plans of the Russian scientist Alexander Bolonkin, who emigrated to the USA where he launched into a frenzy of invention. Bolonkin dreams on an epic scale, from a transport system based on cables suspended from airships to an enormous dome to protect cities from hurricanes and nuclear attack to a (perfectly serious) patent application for 'human immortality'. In 2006 he co-authored a paper that proposes a gigantic wind dam should be built in Antarctica. This would be a huge tethered fabric fence around 50m high and up to 1000km long, channelling winds into ground-level turbines that could generate 450GW of electricity: around ten times the total demand of the UK. Suddenly a wind dam looks totally feasible.

ILLUSTRATOR LINDSEY YANKEY has itchy feet. Born in the US, she's currently passing through London on her way to New Zealand. As she travels she's picking up illustration jobs here and there, but promises she'll get serious on her return to America...

WHAT ARE YOUR INFLUENCES?

Good Dog Carl by Alexandra Day really captivated me as a child and I loved the bold illustrations by Clement Hurd in Goodnight Moon. I also remember enjoying Beatrix Potter and spending ages poring over the pictures in a massive red velvet Disney storybook. My art teacher Mrs. Johnson was a big encouragement. She seemed to really like me, so I really liked her! I also relish strange encounters, nature, animals, the weather...

HOW DID YOU GET INTO ILLUSTRATION?

I started out studying Elementary Education and then switched to Art Elementary Education before settling on Visual Communications at the University of Kansas in the US. It was all a part of finding my way. One afternoon I was walking home and the idea for a story, about the sun and the moon, popped into my head. I scribbled down the idea and began making pictures based on the narrative. The next semester I changed my major for the final time.

WHAT'S HAPPENING NOW?

This year I've done some illustrations for a design agency called Whiskey Design, then I discovered Amelia's Magazine and did a couple of illustrations for the online magazine. I just left an amazing job working in the conservation lab at my university library, repairing books and maps; it was great to be surrounded by so many types of books and kept me fully immersed in printed material. When I return to the States I'm going to start seriously pursuing illustration jobs.

WHAT MATERIALS DO YOU WORK WITH?

Papers, oil paints and coloured pencils, mainly. I'd say I'm pretty crafty. I make books and jewellery and I've done a bit of art direction for a short film. I like producing artwork with my hands because there is still so much you can do in real life that you can't do on a computer. I painted the Wind Dam on wood and only did basic touching up in Photoshop.

HOW DID YOU GET ON WITH THE WIND DAM?

I like digging into an illustration to find a story or reason behind things but it was quite difficult to research the Wind Dam as it hasn't been constructed yet! I had to base the illustration around the presumption that it is dependent on something to support it, so I chose to hang it from hills. I like working with a narrative and because I've become more interested in the incorporation of handwritten text I decided to include notes made during the developmental stage of the illustration. I think this project reinforces the idea that everyone needs to be involved in shaping a new future; not just architects, environmentalists, and scientists. Artists and designers do too.

WHAT MAKES YOU ANGRY?

Littering always makes me angry. Everybody does it; old people, kids, mums. It's just so annoying! I lived in Walthamstow, London during the summer and it was quite disturbing because there were hardly any trash cans. I think we need better education. My grandmother taught me not to be a litterbug; and I didn't drop stuff because I didn't want to make her mad.

WHAT MAKES YOU HAPPY?

Fresh air, friends, rock climbing, hiking, slack lining (which is like walking a tightrope) orange juice, people-watching, mangos and avocados. Yosemite National Park in California

www.lindseyyankey.com

Kansas, US

is the most beautiful place I've ever been. The world would be a better place if everybody stopped and relaxed to watch the sunset. How amazing would that be? I seriously think it could be a community effort, such a good idea. We need to relax and slow down!

SHOULD CREATIVES TAKE RESPONSIBILITY?

Well, on a personal level I'm pretty good at taking bags to the supermarket, I recycle and I ride my bike so I feel like I'm pretty aware of what I should do. It should be a designer's first priority to consider the environment, so we shouldn't just create more stuff to buy. It's easier to sneak the idea of responsibility into people's lives by making ecological choices popular. I think we're heading in a positive direction.

WHAT DOES THE FUTURE HOLD FOR YOU?

Because I've studied both education and illustration I would like to write and illustrate children's books. I'd love to illustrate for another author but I've also started to develop my own storylines, fun stories with structure, substance and a moral – without being too preachy. It's a fine line, but for instance Shaun Tan manages to broach serious subject matter in a way that appeals to all ages. He's not afraid to challenge his readers with important issues like immigration and colonisation, and his illustrations are so deeply-layered that I can look at one of his books for the twentieth time and still spot something I haven't noticed before. Kids like it, adults like it, it's a multi-generational thing.

HOLY MACKERAL A MONSTER!!
NO, IT BE FRIENDLY
ELECTRICITY
seacurrent's energy
ENERGY TO SHIP
SMOOTH FLOW TO TURBINE GENERATOR
BULGE WAVE
DEFRACTION DISPLACES ENERGY

THE **IDEA** *behind a new wave energy converter from professors Rod Rainey and Francis Farley is appealingly simple. Just float a long water-filled rubber sausage under the waves. As waves advance, the pressure on the sausage drives the water inside it towards a turbine in a travelling 'bulge wave'. No, it's not called the Sausage. Their new invention is known as the Anaconda.*

The Anaconda has very few parts and is made of rubber, so it is light and cheap and there is less scope for deterioration in the harsh marine environment. In fact the inventors suggest that if the worst comes to the worst it will just get washed up on a beach from where it can be retrieved, patched up, just like a punctured bike tube, and sent out to sea again. The plan is to float a series of Anacondas a few miles offshore in water up to 100m deep, where they can capture the energy of large sea swells. Each Anaconda measuring 6m wide and 200m long would be capable of producing 1MW of energy.

Like most wave technologies the Anaconda has some very close relations. For example, in 1919, Chester Braselton of New York patented a device that used pumps powered by a series of submerged bags. In 1967 Marcel Semo of Massachusetts patented the notion of a line of bladders on the sea-bed and in 1979, an Englishman, Michael French, patented plans for a flexible tube that, like the Anaconda, floats just below the waves. In 2002, Charles Carroll of Princeton was granted a patent for an Energy Harvesting Eel that wriggles in the current just like a genuine eel, the motion directly producing electricity by the piezoelectric effect (the ability of some materials to generate electricity when flexed). None of these ideas have yet seen the light of day, but the times are a-changing and tests using the Anaconda have been promising.

RBS
MARKET GARDEN

Royal Bank of Sustainability for Amelia's Magazine
and Platform at C Words, Arnolfini

LIV BARGMAN currently lives in Montgomery, Wales but dreams of finding a studio in a thronging city, either London or Bristol. She is influenced by the Bright Young Things of the 20's, Cecil Beaton, early 20th century cinema and the Shropshire Hills. Life at University College Falmouth was all about sea shanties and pasties. Publishing her first book in France seems like a good idea because croissants are the same shape as pasties...

LOVING ILLUSTRATION.

I love illustration because it's not self-indulgent, it's for everybody. It's such a welcoming art. Fine art can be a little bit alienating: I work at a gallery and I sometimes find it hard to engage with the art, but illustration is egalitarian and seen by loads of people. Everyone needs colour and creativity in their lives; when people look at nice imagery it makes them happy and often links them back to their childhood. I'm inspired by nostalgic, handmade things, as well as objects remembered from my childhood. It's important that people get together and make stuff, be it cake or crafts. I like that lovely tactile feeling of a one-off creation.

PENTEL AND CONTÉ.

I mainly work in pencils and felt: my favourite felt tips are Pentel Colour Pen Fine Point because the pigment is really strong, and I've recently rediscovered the amazing smudgy Conté crayons. For a pixellated effect similar to what you get with screen-printing I cut up newspapers and blow bits up. I'm attracted to well loved old books and impressions from times gone by like the signs you see painted on the side of a disused factory, so I pick colours that look as if they have been battered and worn down. When I look at my work on the computer I usually need to jiggle it around and change the composition

then scan extra bits and add them to the illustration. I'd love to learn screen-printing because I never had the opportunity at university.

LADYBIRD BOOKS AND REN AND STIMPY.

I have over a hundred Ladybird books that I have hunted down in charity shops. My favourite ones are about science, I love the way they are educational, and ergonomically designed (for people with teeny hands). Ronald Searle books were shoved under my nose when I was a child and both my grandmother and my mum sold antiques and vintage clothes in Shrewsbury market. I'm inspired by the graphics in old cookery books, anything that is an archeological dig into social history. As a child I spent a lot of time amongst old things so they have infiltrated my being, but I also like the aesthetics of old computer games graphics and I watched a lot of Ren and Stimpy in the 90's which warped my mind somewhat. French illustrator Frédérique Bertrand and American scribbler Jeremyville do 'peculiar' well. On the patterning side of things I'm a big fan of Sami tribal designs.

GREENGAGED AND PRIMARK.

The Greengaged conference on sustainability was a big eye-opener. I volunteered to illustrate the day themed around Crafting Mass Production, about how craft sensibilities and values can be brought to a mass production scale. I listened in on all workshops and presentations, taking notes and sketching in one colour (green of course). I love the idea that you don't have to buy brand-new things, you can use what's already there; go to a charity shop instead of buying something new. After Greengaged I thought "I'm never going to buy anything new ever again!" Primark gives me the creeps. Maybe in the future I'll set up my own printing press using vegetable inks and recycled paper sourced from Three Trees Don't Make a Forest, which is an online resource for ethical design.

CRISIS IN CAPITALISM.

Corporations are bigger than government, but it seems that corporations have underestimated people, who now realise they can grow their own food and build up a small business without having to use unsustainable means. We might not make tons of cash in five minutes if we act responsibly but everything needs to slow down in order for the earth to cope, and chances are that life will be all the better for it. A good idea is to start baking your own bread – there won't be any horrible chemicals in it and it's relaxing.

COLLABORATION.

I graduated alongside several other children's illustrators, Sophie Foster, Kate Hindley and Sarah Brown and we've decided to do a book to promote ourselves based on the Exquisite Corpse, which was a concept developed by the Surrealists where one person draws the head of a character, another the torso and so on without looking at the previous contributions, until a whole character is produced. The pages of a ring-bound book will be divided into three so that you can flip between all the characters to create new ones. It comes from this cheesy conceptual idea of us all merging together! Collaboration is exciting, particularly when it is with creatives in other disciplines such as photography and graphic design – I think that everything is gradually merging together anyway. I'd like to do something on a large scale in three dimensions, like illustrator Cristina Guitian, who does amazing murals on old brick walls.

NORWEGIAN FJORDS.

My illustration of the Archimedes Bridge shows a floating footbridge that is held submerged beneath the water's surface by Archimedes' Principle. The buoyancy of the water holds it up, gravity keeps it down and it's low-impact on the environment because it doesn't touch the bottom of the river. It's still in development but models have been built in the Norwegian fjords, in small villages where normal bridges couldn't be built because of the costs. I found it a bit disheartening that people write so many negative things about new technologies in development. Sustainable design needs so much support right now.

SOLENODONS.

Anything furry with a funny snout tickles me quite pink, for example the incredibly rare Solenodon from the West Indies, which is the only mammal in the world that delivers venom through its teeth. Feline creatures are so sneaky and devious. I dare say that my cat Timmay influences some of my characters, but I need to work on drawing animals well to get work doing children's books. You need to have a moral in kid's stories in the UK but in France, for some reason, there's a lot more scope.

OWL AND MAGPIE.

I'm going to concentrate on children's stories; I've written one called Owl and Magpie (working title). The Owl – being nocturnal – likes to stay up all night playing computer games, but the Magpie spoils his fun every morning by playing her dawn song so that the sun rises. This scuppers Owl's plans, so he steals the instrument required to call in the sunrise, thus making it night forever. This has terrible consequences; the plants die and people get hurt because they can't see anything. The Owl feels guilty and realises there is a balance to things so he gives the instrument back. I might decide to use human characters to allow for greater depth and facial expression. The story and I still need to do some development...

Montgomery,
Wales

CETO IS THE PRIMORDIAL SEA GODDESS OF GREEK MYTHOLOGY, personification of the power of the ocean. And CETO is also a Cylindrical Energy Transfer Oscillating unit – not quite as fabulous a translation eh? CETO hails from Australia and lives on the bottom of the seafloor. It consists of a submerged balloon-like float attached to a piston that captures its motion and drives high pressure water ashore to power a turbine and provide desalinated water. Because the float is completely underwater nothing is visible from shore and storm damage is avoided. Built from rubber and steel it is cheap to produce and all delicate machinery is kept safely on land. Following a successful prototype test in 2006 a large commercial demonstration is currently underway in the waters of Garden Island off Western Australia.

The first CETO plant will consist of rows of bobbing balloons on the seafloor, enough to generate 5MW of power. It is claimed that all the freshwater needs of the southern states of Australia could be covered by a CETO wave farm measuring 1.5km squared. In a country which is already experiencing severe droughts this is a bold and exciting claim.

Another project that is nearing agreement focuses on the island of Mauritius, which is buffeted by waves of a suitable height and power throughout the year. CETO will be tested at five sites, in total producing 200MW, which covers 50% of the electricity consumption of the island. The costs are comparable with a wind project of the same size, so this is exciting news for island dwellers everywhere.

Two of Hearts for Amelia's Magazine Shelter Card Quilt

Royal Bank of Sustainability for Amelia's Magazine
and Platform at C Words, Arnolfini

IF YOU WANNA KNOW what the precociously talented illustrator Louise McLennan is up to, just check online. She's been making her own websites since the tender age of ten and updates her blog regularly with a stream of consciousness that gives away the innermost workings of her extraordinary mind. "I'm L.E.McLennan" announces her online bio, "and I do a whole lotta drawings a whole lotta the time. I like to enter illustration competitions which I've had some good luck with." This is something of an understatement; she's submitted work to countless call outs, finding them by searching for 'zine' 'competition' and 'open brief' in google – including one for... Kleenex Tissues. Next to her entry for the Lazy Oaf competition it says: "This is why I say enter competitions, you get the glory of winning... I know I actually came runner up, but I still feel like I won!" Her piece for Lazy Oaf? A multiple eyeball necklace, an homage to the 'eye series' by Brooklyn artist Lauren Albert.

Talented way beyond her years (she's barely left her teens), Louise is completely self-taught. "I am not an illustration student," proclaims her website "I do information systems technology/multimedia development." She's retaining a marginal interest in her course because she might get to do animation and "3D stuff" at some point, but most of the time it just gets in the way; "stupid uni work getting in the way of my many projects," she

laments on Twitter. Her love of drawing began at nursery school, where she would draw endless pictures of her dad coming home through the garden at the end of the day. A close relationship with her father is evident – he accompanies her to the Shelter House of Cards exhibition private view in London. There are artists on her mother's side of the family but Louise is pretty scathing of the artists' scene in Aberdeen. "Everyone draws landscapes." School wasn't much better, "I didn't learn anything about art, we just painted endless pots."

Don't count on her website reading the same statement for very long; she's incredibly adept at making the most of the internet, uploading to numerous websites simultaneously and switching things around with alarming regularity. "I'm never happy with the way things look," she explains. Previous personal websites GalaxyTwo and Vampire Batman have gone the way of the redirected url, but she seems fairly settled on the current one bearing her own name. Of her talent for working with computers, Louise is typically nonchalant; "I just taught myself – looked it up and figured it out." (Remember that this was at age ten.) She recommends the free templates from Indexhibit for designing websites easily, and deviantART, the first port of call to post many of her doodlings, for finding the best new artists. It was on this community that she first stumbled upon fellow featured illustrator Justin Wallis, of whom she is a big fan. "There's a strange selection of work on there but if you google an unusual term like 'psychedelic' then that usually throws up some interesting stuff." Louise always comments beneath the pictures she likes in deviantART. She was recently accepted onto the Behance website as well, which is slightly less egalitarian, in that it has a screening process which she is not too keen on; "People get too fixed in what they like, so there's no room for new things."

Louise's style is characterised by a mixture of black marker pen, vector gradients and clashing coloured patterns that invariably involve lots of triangles. It's a style that she first chanced upon aged

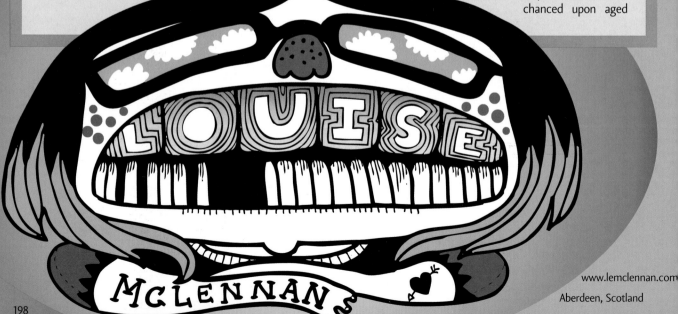

www.lemclennan.com
Aberdeen, Scotland

a comic called Fat Lemon with her best friend Erin – "I don't need any other friends" – and recently contributed to Test Everything zine.

Louise takes most of her inspiration from sci-fi, from TV shows like Futurama, Star Trek "but I'm not a Trekkie!" and Judge Dredd, and also from movies like Event Horizon, Stargate and Escape from New York which she will sometimes doodle along to, whilst watching. She's interested in the extremely distant technologies of the future, "we don't know what it will look like so I can make stuff up." Her drawings based in a made up galaxy called Star of Wonder (after a Sufjan Stevens song of the same name) look at the balance between the 'tribal' and 'mechanical' world. "One is more in touch with nature and the other one is more of a dictatorship," she explains. "The story is about how we need to bring the two together, but they currently exist separately and the mechanical wants to take over the tribal." The moral is that they could work better together in harmony. More ambitiously she recently produced a zine called Oil Spill, which explores our dependance on oil. "It forced me to draw in the same style for ten pages!" she smiles. Why did she chose to illustrate this subject? "Earth is our only planet, so we should look after it."

In terms of showing the alternative technologies that we might be using in the near future, Louise is most interested in imagined cities and futuristic landscapes featuring rotating wind buildings, solar towers, hidden underwater energy... and exploding algae monsters. It's a no brainer to commission her for the front cover, even if it is the first time she's had any input from an art director. She's quick to adapt and work within fairly strict parameters, which is quite an achievement for someone who says of competition briefs: "I often draw what I think I should enter first, then actually enter something totally different."

She has no plans to leave Aberdeen. "Now that we have the internet I don't need to go anywhere."

nine. "Until recently I was drawing Anime but I didn't enjoy it so don't know why I was doing it, I've been much happier since I returned to the style I had as a kid." The style of an individual picture depends on the medium. "My spacey tribal stuff looks better done by hand, then I trace the images with vectors on the computer." Pictures created completely on the computer have no outlines and lots of colour gradients. She has just started to mix up these two techniques, to great success, which could explain her love for Clor and Beck, who make stylistically mashed up music. She works fast, spending no more than a few hours on a picture, and is fairly certain now where her style lies; part of a running commentary on her blog about an illustration in progress reads: "It's a bit over 'kawaii' at the moment but I'll be sure to slap Louisey-ocity all over it (ie. TRIIIANGLES)" Kawaii being the term for overly cutesy Japanese designs. She produces

POND-SCUM, the kind that grows in stagnant pools, could call a halt on climate change. There are perhaps 300,000 species of the green glop more politely known as algae, a term used to describe pretty much all primitive green things, from lichens to seaweed. Surely it sounds too good to be true?! Well, the scum sure is clever, for not only is it extremely nutritious and fast growing but it can also manufacture oil directly from carbon dioxide (CO_2), water and sunshine. In principle that should mean we could pipe the dirty CO_2 produced by conventional power stations into huge ponds and make lots of fabulously handy oil out of it. But there must be a catch, right? Otherwise we would be doing it already…

It turns out that people have been intermittently pouring money into the idea for many years, often giving up along the way. With the prospect of Peak Oil fast approaching or possibly even behind us, there has recently been another surge of interest in algae. No wonder, really – algae can produce more than half its weight in oil and can grow 30 times faster than a conventional crop, meaning that it can be harvested every 1-10 days.

Now for the bad news. It's an extremely messy business which scientists are currently trying to remedy by engineering algae to release oil onto the surface of water without the need to be pulverised, but what works well in the rarefied confines of a laboratory often refuses to work properly on a large scale. Nature is not so easily tamed

and dastardly forms of wild algae are liable to penetrate open ponds (not to mention the reverse problem where genetically modified algae escapes into the wild). Closed ponds or tube systems, known as photobioreactors, can cause more problems because they lack light and dead algae are liable to block up the system. Algae thrive best in sunny climes, and ponds take up a lot of land that might be considered marginal but doubtless has an alternative use for the locals.

In spite of all these challenges we've an oil addiction to feed and so the new gold rush is on. Since most of the oil we use today comes from ancient algae… what better place to look? One approach might be to ask what surfaces are already exposed to the sun, and since leaked algae is relatively harmless, visionary architects and engineers are wondering how algae could be grown on buildings. Just think, our cities could soon look like the legendary hanging gardens of Babylon, once considered to be one of the Seven Wonders of the World.

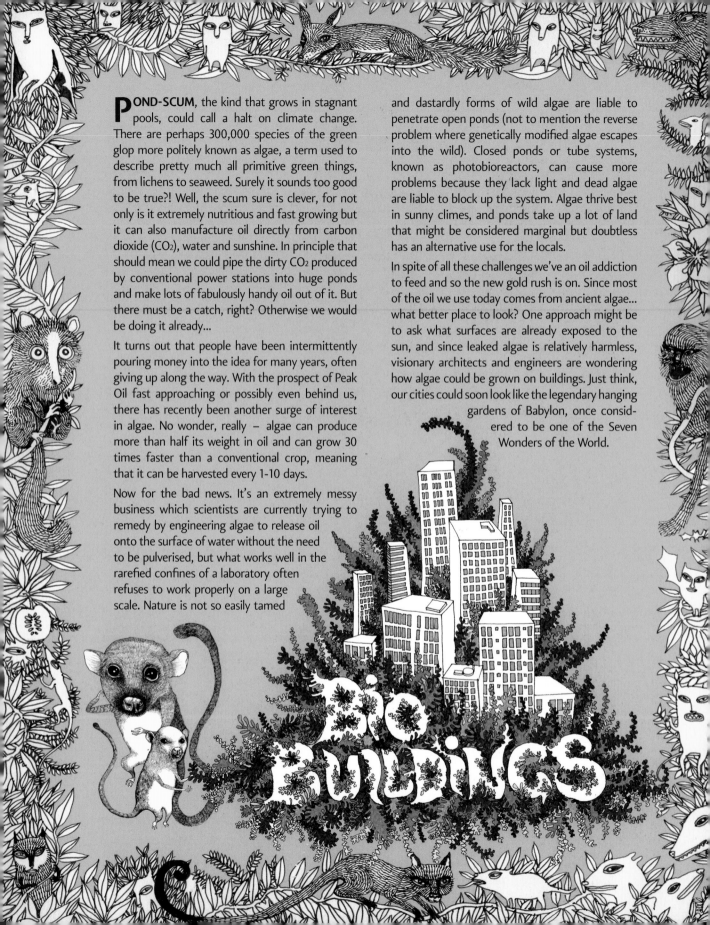

Bio BUILDINGS

MAGDA BOREYSZA

POLISH ILLUSTRATOR AND ANIMATOR MAGDA BOREYSZA grew up in Lund in southern Sweden before moving to Scotland in 2003 to study for a BA in Animation at the Edinburgh College of Art. She liked it so much that she has stayed on to do a post grad. Her degree encompassed traditional techniques such as hand-drawing and stop-motion puppets so she soon found out that illustration came naturally to her. If she had to live in another time she would choose a place of lively cultural activity, a time of possibilities, "during the Renaissance, or in Paris during the 1920's – when cinema and photography were young." Or she'd move to the future, "where I would travel between stars with my sentient machine friends."

How do you live more lightly?

I cycle a lot and I became vegan twelve years ago, in large part for environmental reasons. Meat and dairy products just waste so many resources it's shocking. People often go, 'I could never be vegan because I love cheese too much.' My answer is: 'Be as vegan as you can. Do your best. And when you really crave cheese just have some.' It's not about some notion of purity, but about adopting a lifestyle that is easier on the environment and respectful towards our fellow animals.

What does your vision of a better future look like?

Technology would evolve to become more harmonious with the environment and nature would be an integral part of every city: we would have buildings covered in plants, rooftop gardens on every house and lots of trees in the streets. I'd like to see more animals in the city, and of course people would cycle more frequently or travel by tram. Solar power would be used for most things, along with pedal power for individual needs like mobile phones.

How did you work on this illustration?

Illustration is a private affair for me, it's like dreaming as I try to let my subconscious take over. I sit up at night with tea, listening to music or the radio... then I'll start with one detail, and the rest kind of grows out of that. The illustration of algae-covered buildings came together very quickly because I was excited about engaging with a constructive solution. I decided on the basic layout of the image and then improvised the different characters and the wild-growing algae. The idea was very simple, but allowed me to have fun with the details, which is what I like to do. I use a lot of source images for inspiration: photos, postcards, picture books and my digital image collection. In the past I've worked mostly in black and white, but throughout this past year I've used more and more colour in my work. When I made the illustrations for this anthology I tried to make them lively and colourful. I experimented a lot and it was a good experience.

What excites you at the moment?

Right now I'm really excited by space exploration. I made a comic about Laika, the first dog in space, and I've been reading lots of sci-fi by the likes of Alastair Reynolds, M. John Harrison and William Gibson. I'm fascinated by physics, astronomy, maths and the future of technology so I've been reading books that feed my interests: Chaos: Making a New Science by James Gleick, Pale Blue Dot: A Vision of the Human Future in Space by Carl Sagan and Douglas R. Hofstadter's Gödel, Escher, Bach: An Eternal Golden Braid.

Where do you look to for inspiration?

I always have something to look at because I keep a handy collection of art postcards stuck to the wall above my desk. I love going to museums to draw the exhibits, especially the Natural History Museum in London and the Pitt Rivers Museum in Oxford. I walk around the museum with my sketchbook and draw whatever happens to catch my eye, often the ceremonial masks, stuffed animals, skeletons or specimens in the anatomical collections. Afterwards I use the observational drawings as a basis for more imaginative pieces like the drawing of a sorceress hypnotising a strange creature. I also like to while away hours at the local art library, where I pick out a stack of art and photography books and draw things I like in my sketchbook. I love the work of Moomin creator Tove Jansson and comics are one of my favourite things; anything by American Charles Burns

Two of Hearts for Amelia's Magazine Shelter Card Quilt

and French comic artist David B. I've just finished reading Shaun Tan's The Arrival which is a really beautiful and moving graphic novel. I wish I'd drawn it! It gave me some good insights into visual storytelling.

Have you written any stories?

At the moment I'm working on an animated film influenced by my interest in science called A Game of String. I'm very pleased with it so far: it's a story about two characters who live in an observatory and watch the whole universe through a telescope. They can see everything from the smallest particles to the biggest galaxy clusters. The most interesting part is trying to visualise and draw things like superstrings, quantum wave-particles and atoms. It's pretty much impossible so I use my poetic licence.

How do you network with other people?

I'm part of the Forest, which is an alternative arts and event space in Edinburgh. My strategy is to get my stuff seen in any way, so through the years I've done a lot of events posters, murals etc. for free, and this in turn has generated actual commissions. It helps that I tap into a lot of different scenes: zine fairs, comic shops, galleries, animation and conventional illustration. Toastycats is my pet zine project and it's tremendous fun. Each issue contains some short humorous comic strips, a few illustrations and a chunk of my long-running, more serious graphic story The Seed. It's an enigmatic tale, and the less said about it, the better. So far I've printed four issues of Toastycats but it's a bit irregular due to college commitments. I distribute it through comic and gallery shops as well as through my online shop.

What it's like to be an illustrator these days?

Being an artist today is easy. When else, in human history, would I have received government funding to mess around with cartoons at college? When else were people able to sell their handmade jewellery online or print their own zines? The only difficulty arising from all these opportunities is that there are so damn many of us now. The competition is fierce.

LOOSE CANNONBALL WAVE POWER

IS there a way to capture huge quantities of free energy from the sea using an engine with just one moving part? That's the question my father Bruce Gregory found himself asking when he started researching renewable technologies for this very book. And because he once trained as an engineer he couldn't resist trying to figure out how this might be done. Here, then, is the wild card of the Anthology.

Standard wind turbines work on the very simple principle that three blades must be spun to push a magnet past a copper wire to generate an electric current. What is the simplest possible way to push magnets past copper wires with waves in the ocean? Imagine a giant ball weighing several tons that sits in the middle of a huge floating hemispherical bowl which is tethered to the sea-bed. The ball and the bowl both have smooth surfaces and as the waves pass, the bowl rocks and the giant ball rolls around the bowl. Just under the surface of the ball is an array of powerful magnets. Just under the surface of the bowl is an array of copper coils. As the ball rolls the magnets move past the coils and voila: electric

current. All you need then is a lid on the bowl to stop the ball from falling out, a circuit in the bottom of the ball to transform the current into power and a cable to the shore. Oddly enough this is exactly the patent that Raymond Rowe applied for in California in 1985, but intended to power buoys on a very small scale.

But what about a whole wave farm of perhaps a hundred bowls, each about 9m across, with giant concrete balls in each measuring around 1.8m across? Okay, so there are a few catches. If there is a lot of bad weather the ball might jump up and down too much and grind down the bowl so the contact area between ball and bowl must be kept small. The magnets must move past enough coils at a fast enough speed (approximately 9m per second) to keep up a sufficient power output. Surely not so hard considering that this is approximately the same speed as a bike descending a gentle hill. And there are other niggles to iron out. But what an idea.

Bruce calls this the Loose Cannon Project, because when a cannon breaks loose of its harness on a ship's deck in heavy weather the result is chaos. Loose cannon is also, aptly, a term for a maverick. He is keen to point out that over 1500 patents have been published for different kinds of wave engines and (despite some exciting advances) not one has yet succeeded in being scaled up for commercial use. So the likelihood that he has invented something that could change the course of renewable energy is highly improbable. Still, someone has to do it, and why not my crazy inventor dad?

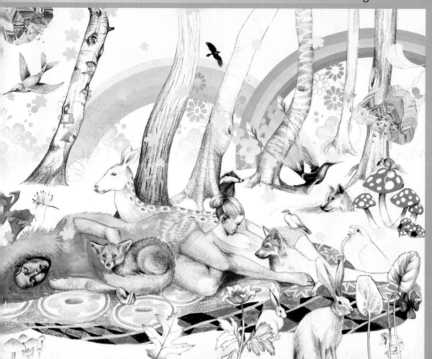

Two of Hearts for Amelia's Magazine Shelter Card Quilt

BIRDS, INSECTS, MAMMALS and beautiful girls frolic together under vividly coloured skies and multi-hued rainbows in Mia Overgaard's utopian illustrations. A Copenhagen-based illustrator who graduated from the Danish Design School in 2006, Mia spent a few years in New York freelancing on editorial illustration for an impressive number of publications before returning to Denmark in 2009. Although her fashion illustrations depicting beautiful women make their home on the glossy pages of upmarket magazines she is no newbie to illustrating for ethical concerns, having recently designed all the publicity with Amelia for Climate Camp in London during 2009.

In the morning I need a cup of tea or coffee next to me to get going and sometimes I light a candle to help me concentrate, although I'm working in a shared studio with several textile designers so I'm a bit worried about burning the building down! Music is a vital source of inspiration and at the moment I am listening to Cat Power, Bat For Lashes, Anthony & The Johnsons, Leonard Cohen and Fiona Apple. To speed things up I listen to Fleet Foxes and old hippie bands like Van Morrison and Crosby, Stills, Nash & Young. I recently discovered the Norwegian musician Kim Hiorthøy, who makes the most wonderful minimalistic music, perfect for getting my work moving.

How did your career as an illustrator start?

Right after university I got an unpaid internship with graphic designer and fashion illustrator Lisa Grue at Underwerket. It only lasted one month but it gave me an insight into the 'real' world of illustration and I learned a lot from her, especially about how to run a successful business and claim credit for your work as an artist. After that I started working freelance for magazines and record companies.

What was your first illustration commission?

My first paid illustration job was for an album sleeve for French record company The Perfect Kiss Records. I actually went to meet up with them in Paris and it all felt very professional and exciting. I remember sitting in the metro on my way to the meeting with my portfolio under my arm thinking "This is it, this is what I want to do!"

When you sit down to work what are the vital things you need?

Where do you do your illustrations?

I've just moved into a communal studio because I think it's crucial to share my work, get feedback and be inspired by others. I have books and pencils, watercolours and yarn (I knit to relax) spread all over the place. My computer sits on an antique desk that I bought in America and painted candyfloss-pink. I have some of my work glued to the wall – so that I don't forget what it is I am doing – and small porcelain figurines of animals on the shelves to keep my creative spirits up!

What else inspires your creativity?

My friends, people on the street, photographs in magazines, music, art and the wonders of nature. My self initiated work comes out of a vision of something beautiful or interesting in my head which I then try to catch on paper. I am fascinated by a mix of very urban, high culture, man-made stuff and the very beautiful basic elements of nature: sea, sky, land, flora and fauna. That clash of diversity appeals to me.

Copenhagen, Denmark

Mia Maarie Overgaard

www.miaovergaard.com

Do you keep a sketchbook?

I have several sketchbooks on the go at once but they are quite personal so I don't like showing them to anybody. I just took a peek at the first page of the nearest sketchbook and I found a bikini model and a colourful pattern. Some of them are inspirational books where I gather the things that inspire me; cut–outs from magazines, photos that I took, candy paper, postcards. Others I save for getting layouts right, for research, or for observational drawings. I'm not the kind of artist that walks around with a sketchbook all the time but for a period I loved going to the zoological gardens with my little chair to sit and draw the animals. When I left I always felt sorry for the animals having to live in such a small space so now I have stopped going there.

How do you create a finished illustration?

Usually I use a lot of white sheets of paper for one final artwork. My main media are pencils, watercolour and Photoshop. In a very detailed piece I tend to draw or paint a lot of the elements separately and then scan them into Photoshop where I resize and move them around to make sure things look right; working on the computer like this saves time. I try to make illustrations that are feminine, delicate and colourful. I like making detailed drawings of people and animals in dream worlds, beautiful but with ugly undertones.

How did you find living in America?

The move from tiny Denmark to humongous North America was the most exciting experience I have been through so far. Though I knew from the start that the stay would only be for two years – I followed my boyfriend out there on the agreement that we would return once he finished his post doc – it felt both challenging and a bit frightening at first. But I realised after some months had passed that I had this feeling of being embraced by the world; that it was okay to actually go ahead and take a chance and it was possible to move to a totally different part of the world and feel welcomed. Maybe that was because of the American mentality, or perhaps it would have felt the same moving to India, I don't know. I do know that being based in the States for awhile really helped my career and now I have great agents both in New York and in London.

How did you find the process of illustrating sustainable energy?

I was attracted to the challenge of making an initially boring and nerdy topic like sustainable energy interesting, so I decided to show the beauty of sustainable energy and how it could be integrated into our natural world. At first I had a bit of a hard time sizing elements in the picture, but decided that it didn't matter too much if the perspective wasn't perfect. Initially the bowls were much smaller than they are now, so when I found out that they were supposed to be nearly ten meters in diameter I had to resize all the teeny tiny animals like butterflies and beetles. It was quite a challenge to get it looking natural without being boring or crammed but I find that challenges often make a job more fun to work on.

Are there ways in which you try to protect the environment?

In my own little way I try to consider the environment in my day to day life. There is nothing like a nice bicycle ride and I have always loved to take the train. I bring my own bags when I go grocery shopping, remember to turn off the lights, eat ethical foods and use environmentally friendly detergents and cleaning products. I hope in the close future that I will get to have my own garden, where I would grow vegetables and fruit and keep chickens.

poster and stickers for Climate Camp at Blackheath, London in 2009

What do you think would make the world a better place?

Personally, I would love to be able to fill my lungs with clean, fresh air even when I'm in the city, and I would love there to be less noise coming from heavy traffic on the roads. In my vision of a better future there would be fewer cars and trucks and more bikes ridden by healthy, happy people with blushing cheeks and wind in their hair!

How was the publicity for Climate Camp 2009 created?

I combined bold graphic silhouettes of direct action – bicycles, ladders, bolt cutters, D-locks and tripods – with elements of nature, images of sustainability and the causes of climate change. I used a very simple colour palette and the result was very different from my usual stylistic approach. Because I have never been involved in any direct climate action myself it was beneficial to have Amelia as a direct link to the whole project. She is an explosion of ideas and whenever I felt emptied out she would come back to me with new views on the work. I think the end result expresses the ideas behind Climate Camp very well.

What is it like to know that your images have become symbolic of a direct action movement against climate change?

When I first submitted my work for the open brief it never occurred to me that my illustrations might spread to different Climate Camps across the world so it was a pleasant surprise to find out that they had. I guess I expected there to be more creatives involved in voluntary work for the environment across the globe, but maybe there is a lack of artistic people willing to contribute their talents towards a good cause. For me it is just one link in the chain of actions that I take to try and save what I can of this beautiful world around us; I guess we all need to donate a little bit of our lives to secure a positive future for our descendants.

ONE OF THE BIGGEST ISSUES FACING HUMANITY
is how to live a lower carbon lifestyle, as in actually
live it, inside our homes. Managing the temperature of the
buildings in which we sleep, work and play is one of the single
biggest challenges we face in tackling climate change, given
that buildings – both commercial and residential – contribute
roughly one third of all greenhouse gas emissions. By making
sure that insulation is adequate and lighting and appliances
are energy efficient, emissions from buildings could be cut by
as much as 50%.

Retrofitting housing with effective insulation is an
absolute necessity in parts of the world where most of the
housing stock is old and draughty – more than 80% of
total energy consumption takes place during the lifespan
of a building and only 20% goes into the process of construction. However, in parts of the world that are still developing rapidly it is massively important that the switch
to more energy-efficient building solutions happens right
now. The construction industry is incredibly wasteful, so
it is a priority to find ways of minimising that waste by
recycling old materials and taking advantage of environmentally sensitive options.

Luckily lots of architects are looking at ways to build
energy efficient structures that incorporate micro generation of renewables, using both hi-tech and ultra low
tech solutions. Michael Jantzen opts for the hi-tech route
with his Solar Wind Pavilion for the California State University, which does what it says on the tin and impressively integrates wind and solar power generation along
with harvesting of rainwater. Robert Ferry's Almeisan
Tower imagines a solar tower on top of a cultural centre.
Flights of fancy abound, and are useful in prompting us
to find new ways in which we can integrate energy generation into the very fabric of our lives. But ultimately
the low impact approach is key as well, not only because
it is cheaper and easier to do, but also because we have
centuries of practice in maintaining thermal comfort in a
built environment; all we have to do is look at how things
were done in the past. This, applied alongside the principles of permaculture – looking at natural patterns to
create sustainable human habitats – will go a long way
towards achieving a sustainable future.

Royal Bank of Sustainability for Amelia's Magazine
and Platform at C Words, Arnolfini

SACHIKO MIYAKAWA's imaginary future technology was dreamt up whilst browsing through a bird guide. It's an unmanned air vehicle made from recycled materials that charges by wind turbine and solar cell in the sun above the clouds, flocking like a migrant bird unaffected by the weather. It is equipped with a radar detector to avoid collision with other obstacles and when the charging capacity is full, it glides automatically to one of many bases on earth. From there, power is transferred to schools and communal facilities.

Having completed her studies at Bath Spa University in 2008, "I loved living in Bath, going to the Tea House Emporium, drinking organic cider in Victoria Park and all the fantastic scenery around the town", Sachiko promptly went back home. "I made really cool friends in the UK who I keep in touch with thanks to Facebook." She now resides on "the red circle surrounded by a white rectangle", specifically in the North East of Japan on the Pacific Ocean in idyllic Kesennuma, a town famous for its fish. Living abroad was a culture shock but the possibilities of illustration have been dramatically widened. "It helped to break down stereotypes and now I draw more freely than before."

Sachiko's playful illustrations are busy, loaded with colour. "I like to work in my bedroom because it's such a comfortable place to be that I feel as though it is almost an extension of my body. When I'm drawing I tend to follow my intuition..." First she drafts out the images on "nice smooth paper" with a pencil, before mixing up three or four key

colours based on a chart. "It takes me about half an hour to an hour to get the colours right." She only uses Photoshop to remove dust. "I like working entirely by hand – It's easier for me."

Inspiration is found from reading a wide range of books, including the novels of Haruki Murakami, Japanese Manga, The Frank Book by Jim Woodring and the work of illustrator Yoshitomo Nara. "I like the intense mood he creates. When I was at high school I sympathised with the affronted expressions of his characters – they made me feel better because I could relate to them." She is currently reading Earth Diver by Shinichi Nakazawa, which analyses the geological formation of Tokyo. "He compares a current map of Tokyo with those made in ancient history and deciphers the past spiritual influences onto each place. The guesses are pretty adventurous but they sound plausible." She agrees with the writer that our life is strongly connected to the past.

Sachiko likes to visit museums and galleries but there are more opportunities for being in nature where she lives. "My town is surrounded by thickly forested mountains, wonderful wild flowers and rice paddies. It's beautiful to watch the sun set over the cape." Her day is often broken up by a bicycle ride. "Everyone cycles in Japan, from small kids to old people. However, some roads have to be well-organised for safety!" To relax, she likes nothing better than a visit to an Onsen, a volcanic hot spring spa, where people traditionally bathe and relax. "The best one has amazing views of the Pacific Ocean. It only takes about half an hour to get there from my home so I go there up to ten times a year with my family and friends for a short holiday."

She recently fell in love with the Jōmon Venus, a large clay figure of a pregnant woman created during the Jōmon period of Japanese history, ca.10,000 BC to 300 BC. "The whole shape is so simple

www.loveandhatesati.com

and beautiful, there are no useless shapes: even the negative space is carefully considered." It is believed that this Venus figurine may have been created to wish prosperity on descendants. "I find it really interesting how primitive people visualised their wishes."

A few years ago Sachiko was researching ideas for an essay – the hefty sounding Ethical Design in an Era of Globalisation – when she chanced upon the Mottainai concept, as espoused by Kenyan environmental campaigner and Nobel Prize winner Wangari Maathai. It comes from a Buddhist idea that we do not exist in isolation but are connected together. "It's such a great concept; suddenly I saw the world in a new light. So I strive to appreciate the real worth of things – I appreciate food more and keep my old clothes instead of throwing them away. I cut them up into small pieces which are useful for cleaning up when I use paints. I water the garden which is full of hydrangea, lavender, roses, rosemary, sunflowers, daffodils, tulips, mint and maple leaves."

Sachiko has been proactively participating in the Cool Biz and Warm Biz campaigns which were initiated by the Japanese government to increase energy efficiency. "In the summer I open the windows and doors to let in fresh air so that I don't have to use the air-conditioning. I wear a thin dress when it is warm outside, and in the winter I wear a thick sweater and socks, and I sit in the sun to warm up." She thinks the campaign has been simple but effective. "Many more people in Japan are aware that we need to reduce carbon emissions, so I think it is working."

THE **AQUABUOY,** as it name suggests, superficially resembles the familiar navigational buoy. 3m in diameter, it sits on top of the water, suspended beneath which is a long pump that pushes water through a turbine. Power is brought ashore via an undersea cable from a central collection point in the middle of a 'wave park'.

There were high hopes for this technology from Finavera... and then in 2007 a test buoy sank soon after it was installed a few miles off the Oregon coast: water flooded the flotation section and the pump was unable to cope. Local crab fishermen were quick to decry the technology, claiming that a rusting hulk of iron is now contaminating their fishing grounds. This is untrue: the buoy uses no chemical lubrication and is unlikely to cause any pollution, plus bits of metal can make good homes for wildlife.

However, this debacle pretty much put a stop to Finerva's plans to install a wave park of Aquabuoys (generating 2MW) just off the coast of Humboldt County, California. The California Public Utilities Commission noted that there were unsolved fears over the stability of the Aquabuoy and stated drily that 'there is no industry consensus on the most optimal or most commercially viable wave energy technologies.' In 2009 Finerva quietly released a press statement confirming that they will be concentrating on wind power for the foreseeable future.

It took decades for wind turbines to become efficient, reliable and good value for money – and it's likely to take a similar amount of time for wave energy to become viable. Meanwhile designers and renewable energy companies mutter about the 'dead zone' – the protracted period that lies between the development of promising wave machine prototypes and the emergence of customers who are willing to foot the bills to make them work properly.

SAFFRON STOCKER likes nothing better than a nice plate of chips and beans with cheese on top. She holidays in North Yorkshire, a great place for long walks, climbing rocks and eating traditional cream teas. As a child she entered lots of Blue Peter competitions but she never even won so much as a badge, a fact that still rankles.

Where did you go to university?

I studied Graphic Arts and Design at Leeds Metropolitan which I really enjoyed because it was quite free; it was more like a Fine Arts course then a graphics degree. My final dissertation focused on how the Surrealists used unnerving visual signifiers to put the viewer on edge without knowing why and I used these ideas in my final piece which was an installation inspired by horror films. The room was painted white with a chair in the middle and some plastic ducks swimming down the wall and across the floor. I had shone a light and painted the shadows grey, then painted the ceiling so that it looked like it was sloping down, which were simple but effective ways of creating a surreal atmosphere where normal objects appeared scary.

Did you find work as soon as you left university?

No! The design market is really saturated so I did a lot of internships; it was a question of keep applying, keep applying... My mum trained as a graphic designer and when she graduated employers came to degree shows to handpick students and take them off to a job. It's just not like that anymore, there are thousands of people vying for a small number of jobs.

www.saffronstocker.com

London, UK

Did your mum influence your choice of career?

Well, kind of, but I always thought that what my mum did was a bit boring! Everything had to be type set by hand so she had to rearrange bits of paper with words on them on a bit of card that I wasn't allowed to touch. It seems amazing that graphic design was done like this as recently as within my lifetime. With computers, design has become a completely different ball game: they are of course amazing, but at university I got into the handmade thing so I guess maybe my mum did influence me. We had a fabulous old letterpress and I started using scissors, paper and crayons.

Where did you grow up?

I grew up in Enfield, which had a recycling scheme even when I was a child so I get truly pained if everything isn't separated into the correct bin. I'm a very avid turner offer of appliances so I always go around to check they are switched off at the wall. I live in Hornsey now and I'm quite upset with the fact that Haringey council doesn't even give me a composting bin. I think I might write to them about that!

Where is your studio based?

Everything is done in my bedroom in a lovely old Edwardian house so I'm lucky because I have a fairly large room that can accommodate a lot. There's loads of coloured paper everywhere... but I like having all my stuff around me. If I can't quite figure out how an illustration should go I sit back and look around me... pick up a book maybe, and get inspiration from that... so it seems to work out well.

What inpires you the most?

My parents wouldn't have a television in the house so watching Blue Peter and Tony Hart at friends' houses was my childhood rebellion. Those programmes inspired me to look at the potential use of ordinary objects in my work, rather than relying on expensive materials. Most of my fun came from books or drawing. My parents would get my sister and I to sit down with a stack of paper and pens for entertainment. My sister's a painter now! Nowadays I look at the websites of It's Nice That, FormFiftyFive and Berlin-based Canadian designers Julien Vallée. I don't really get the whole blogging thing myself but I'm trying to get into it. I like going to pound shops to look at all the string and tools, and art shops are good for different coloured cards.

How did you choose to illustrate the technology?

AquaBuoy rises and falls on the waves; the weight in the middle compresses the water, which drives a generator that creates electricity that runs along cables along the seabed and into your living room! Not really – at least not yet – but I'm really glad there are people out there developing such technologies and it's not all some impossible pipe dream. In my vision the fish are telling us how happy they are with this innocuous little buoy, just quietly producing electricity. I did it all with paper and thread holding the pieces together and if you look closely you can see some of the thread; I like that it doesn't look completely flawless. I used a lamp at the side to light it and a camera to record it. It's hard to make illustrations that look tangible on a computer so I only used Photoshop to touch up brightness and colour at the end. I love how there is so much room for happy accidents in a handmade illustration and things usually turn out completely different from how I imagined them.

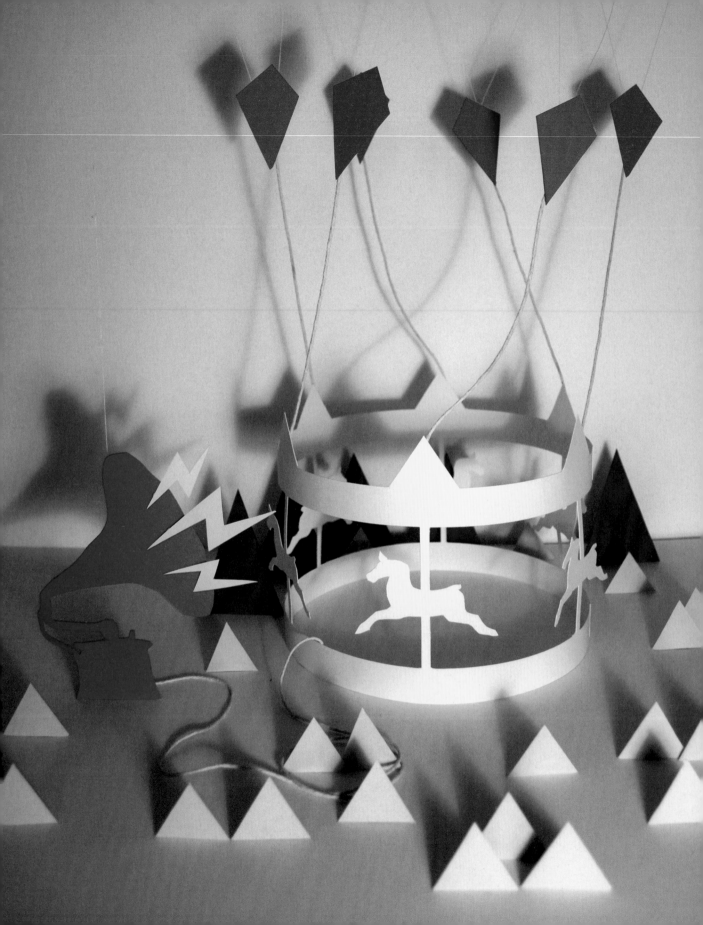

FOR WIND TURBINES to be of any use in the urban environment they need to be cheap, efficient, low maintenance, quiet and – to avoid the wrath of the NIMBYs – barely noticed.

Because the winds around structures tend to be messy, fluctuating in direction and speed, the best kind of wind turbine to build in urban areas is not the familiar three-blade horizontal axis device found in commercial wind farms. Instead a vertical 'egg-whisk' turbine is generally preferable because it works with wind from any angle and has a low starting speed. Quiet Revolution of London is one of many small companies that have developed small vertical turbines; theirs features three twisting, tapered vertical blades made of carbon fibre. As the name of the company hints, the device runs quietly.

However, because rooftop generation is so unreliable the emissions involved in making and installing a small wind turbine can exceed the power savings. There might be a solution. Inventors have often noted that a wind turbine works better if there is a funnel in front of it to collect the wind, so maybe the sides of a pitched roof can operate as a funnel would. Wind striking the roof is deflected upwards and forms a concentrated stream flowing over the roof ridge that can be three times faster than the ambient windspeed. How about making the whole ridge into a turbine?

Former Rolls Royce engineer, Dean Gregory of the Power Collective in Whitby, Yorkshire believes he can do just that, and for his idea he won a half million euro Dutch Green Challenge prize in 2009. The product is called RidgeBlade and it spins on a horizontal axis aligned with the ridge. Because the blade diameter is small it spins fast and no heavy gearing is needed to drive a generator. It is easy to install and its low profile makes it inconspicuous. Dean estimates that the RidgeBlade would only add half a metre to the top of the roof at the most, for which it could produce enough energy for the average household.

But his idea is so new that no trials have yet been reported, thus efficiency and costs are unknown. The swept area of the blades is much smaller than on a conventional turbine which could significantly affect performance and... will the device make the roof vibrate? Perhaps this could be a unique selling point, offering a choice of harmonious sounds for the household below.

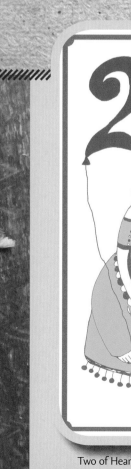

Two of Hearts for Amelia's Magazine Shelter Card Quilt

SINA BECKER is the daughter of a National Opera costume designer who explored food as a medium of expression. "We ate food that looked like castles." Her best friend's mum let them draw on the walls of their topsy-turvy house and melt plastic just to see what would happen. Together they would dress up and invent elaborate stories as they walked through the Black Forest listening to the adventures of mischievous witch Bibi Blocksberg on the radio. Her German parents moved frequently. "I was born in Austria, then we moved to Jerusalem before going back to Vienna." The morning drive to primary school involved passing a glittering mosaic-covered spiral building by visionary architect Hundertwasser. "It was so wonderful that people could walk around and up to the roof garden on top. I love the way that he incorporated nature into his buildings. Imagine if that were to happen in London where land is scarce!"

When she was seven years old the family upped sticks again and moved to Holland before Sina came to the UK to attend the University of Leeds, from which she graduated in 2007. "All the moving around has definitely shaped the way I approach art; being exposed to so many cultures has encouraged me to try new techniques, to play around and have fun." What frightens her most amongst the gloom of environmentalist's predictions? "Oceans rising!" Her years in the Netherlands have clearly affected Sina. "But I'm impressed with how inventive we've become, even creating energy out of our waste." She giggles at the absurd necessity of sorting rubbish into a dozen separate bins, something that she grew up with on the continent where recycling regulations have been in place for many years.

Sina's flat sits atop Queens Park Books, where she works. "Customers expect you to have read everything, so I'm trying to work my way through the stock." It's a small independent bookshop with a cosy atmosphere. "I like it because it has a good sense of community and I get to meet lots of locals, which I think is very important in a big cosmopolitan city like London." Working in the bookshop has opened up a whole new world; "it's like discovering a time machine!" Sina describes with clawed hands the crazy monsters made out of toothpicks and vegetables at events hosted for the local children. "I like to watch simple things being created. I'd love to be one of those people who's proud of their craft, like a furniture maker." She scrunches up her nose. "In fact I want to get away from our whole mass-produced culture."

For as long as she can remember Sina has sketched people. "I have repetitively drawn most characters over a number of years, for instance as a child I obsessively watched all the films featuring actress Romy Schneider and fantasised about wearing lovely ballgowns and having beautiful long hair." She still draws Romy over and over. Her tattooed lady is a fictitious character inspired by a fascination with sailors and a Roald Dahl short story called Skin in which an artist uses a friend's body as a canvas. "When the artist dies his paintings become priceless so all the art dealers try to track down the tattooed man so that they can skin him and display him as a piece of art."

She occasionally collaborates with friends from Leeds – including musicians, and recently designed the cover art for an album by Sky Larkin. Inspiration is found in the form of websites such as It's Nice That, Fffound and This is Process, and Sina is herself a keen blogger. A background in Visual Communication is evident on a site that showcases an eclectic mix of illustra-

tions, photo montages and pictures of her very tidy workspace – she even composes abstract pictures with coloured kids' blocks. Is there any medium she won't tackle? "I'm not patient enough to wait for watercolours to dry. I don't like clay. And I can't think in 3D or moving image." Instead she heads straight for a satisfying black Niceday Fineliner, often to be found lurking in the bottom of her bag, or uses mismatched coloured pencils and the dregs of old pens. She hates restricting herself to any one medium and her style adapts to whatever is lying around. "I save everything from textured paper scraps from the bookshop and cereal boxes to old instruction manuals and Argos catalogues." Sina tells playful stories with her illustrations that are created through a whirlwind process whereby she makes the original sketch, scans it, then opens it in Photoshop to play with colour, often finishing in two or three hours. "I sometimes just have to let my hands get on with it and see what comes out. I work fast." Indeed – that's like a sneeze in creative time. So how does she know when an illustration is done? "Most of my work is spontaneous so I can tell when I'm overdoing it." And for a fresh perspective when things are going stale, Sina holds the work upside down in front of the mirror. "Then you notice all kinds of things, like whether one eye is off in crazyville."

She found the RidgeBlade technology interesting because it was a simple and sensitive design that could be used easily within the urban landscape. "I wanted to demonstrate how life could go on as normal because it doesn't cause any visual or noise pollution." On a similar tangent she selected to draw the Quiet Revolution wind turbines because of their small size, delicacy and suitability to an urban setting. How did she find the process of answering a brief? "I'm usually quite minimalist but Amelia is always like more, more! You have to stay open to new things, challenge yourself."

HUNDREDS OF YEARS AGO, one of the truly tedious domestic tasks was roasting meat in front of an open fire. It was hot, smoky work. Someone had to risk burnt fingers and numbing boredom to slowly turn the spit, so ingenious solutions were found. In Tudor England a dog was set running in something that looked a bit like a large hamster wheel, with an attached belt that would turn the spit. If the dog would not cooperate there was soon another alternative: in his notebooks Leonardo Da Vinci suggested putting a fan in the chimney so that the spit would turn with the rising hot gases; this was the 'smoke jack' first described in detail by an English clergyman, John Wilkins, in 1648.

Australian company Enviromission are planning to put a huge smoke jack in a tremendously tall chimney and replace the fire underneath with a ginormous solar heater in the form of a solar trap (which is essentially just a big plastic tent that traps heat). It's tempting to think that the purpose is to prepare an enormous barbecue, but in fact the aim is to generate cheap renewable electricity.

It's a very inefficient method: only a small amount of the solar energy that is trapped is converted to useful power, but this doesn't matter if the cost is low. The first small solar chimney was built in Manzanares, Spain and ran successfully from 1982 to 1989. The developers propose to build several much larger towers in the imminent future, on cheap land where the sunlight is

intense: a good description of much of the Australian interior. Almost no water is used: which is no minor point given that Australia seems to be gripped by almost permanent drought. However, the first tower mooted for Buronga, New South Wales has now been put on hold whilst plans are put in place to build a couple of towers in Arizona, US where the company is now headquartered.

The solar trap is constructed of strong but lightweight plastic that is held in place by weights as heat builds up during the day and on into the night as radiant heat that has been held in the surrounding ground and air is released. The solar trap will cover an enormous area, approximately 20 square kilometres, underneath which plants will happily grow as if in a giant greenhouse. Hot air rushes past and up the chimney at almost 50 kph, passing through over 30 turbines to produce an estimated 200MW.

A super tall tower is needed to build up the velocity of the hot air hitting the turbines, so the first Enviromission tower to be built will be the tallest man-made structure on Earth: 1000m high, which is more than three times the height of the Eiffel Tower. Because the hot air will cool as it nears the top of the chimney it will be possible to put a viewing platform right at the summit, where tourists can take advantage of the stunning views.

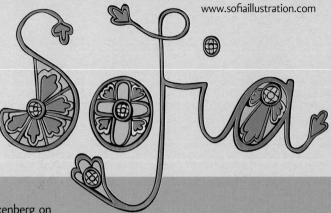

SOFIA ANDERSON grew up in Falkenberg on the south west coast of Sweden. She did an art foundation at Central Saint Martins, then studied graphic design in Sweden at Forsbergs Skola and now reads art history at Stockholm University.

GETTING STARTED.

At Forsbergs I did one day a week on placement at the Electric Boogie Design Coop, where I helped out with design. Some of the first illustrations I worked on were for flatmates who are part of a direct action group called Ofog that campaigns against nuclear power with non-violent 'mischief' at nuclear bases in Norway and Scotland. I didn't get paid but I was hanging out with them a lot and I totally support what they do.

INSPIRATIONAL ARTISTS.

When I was young I got really into Andy Warhol and the whole Pop Art scene, then I discovered the album sleeves for Radiohead by Stanley Donwood and I thought it was really cool the way he hid illustrations inside the CD case. I love the minimalist lines of Jesper Waldersten. I first saw his work in a big Swedish newspaper and I remember seeing this one illustration for an article on paedophilia – using smudged ink on a small girl to show where hands had been – and thinking that it was just so clever. I think I like his work so much because I couldn't possibly work in that way myself. More recently I like the whole New York underground scene and I find the art history theories that I am studying really fascinating.

SOLAR TOWERS AND KITES.

The solar tower is a rad construction; a huge chimney with an even bigger greenhouse at the bottom. I found it interesting that it keeps producing energy during the night, but it was definitely a challenge to try and make the illustration interesting and logical at the same time. I found the idea of kite power really intriguing because even though it is at an early stage of development scientists have already concluded that a relatively small kite could produce enough power for ten homes. Imagine a future where you could drive through the country with all these gorgeous kites floating in the sky above the open fields. These kites could also be welcoming flags at the entrance to a new town or province, like pieces of art generating power.

SUSTAINABILITY.

I don't have a car so I either use public transport or ride my bike. The idea of sustainability is always there in the back of my head so I try to think about what I can do at every point. When I was a child we lived in the countryside so I have always felt close to nature. I go orienteering, running around with a map and a compass in the forest. In Sweden the attitude towards the environment is generally quite good but there are still too many people who don't care about simple things like recycling.

MARKERS AND ELEMENTS.

If I'm going to do a big illustration with lots of elements in it I will conjure up an image in my head and then do a really simple sketch to see where all the different pieces should go. Then I draw them by hand with coloured pencils, water colours and markers, before cutting them out roughly, scanning, composing and brightening them up in Photoshop.

DRAWINGS.

My illustrative style could best be described as realistic, naturalistic and childish. I can't do perfect perspectives so it could definitely be considered somewhat naive. I like to draw people, animals and particularly colourful birds – seabirds, swans, flamingos – at the moment. I've been messing around with putting human heads onto the bodies of birds. I am also fascinated by outer space and space travel because it's so different to the life we know. Hence the illustration for the Two of Hearts brief.

SWEDEN.

I prefer to hang out with artists at the small underground galleries. Loyal is a good gallery for modern art that has just relocated to Malmo in the south of Sweden (which is starting to attract quite a cool scene) and Hangups in Stockholm has fun shows too. Sweden is not that big a country so the illustration scene is quite small and there's a bunch of ten illustrators that are really good and well known and they get most of the good jobs. Some of the successful ones that I like are Liselotte Watkins, Lovisa Burfitt, Kari Moden and Klas Fahlén. If you're a small illustrator like I am then basically you have to take what you can get. I try to do as much as I can but I do more graphic design because that's what pays the best.

Everything is Connected for Amelia's Magazine issue 10

ADVICE.

Sweden is kinda empty so there isn't that much work, and you kind of have to fight to get jobs. I'm not necessarily a good fighter all the time but it's important to keep believing in yourself even when someone doesn't accept your pitch or people don't call back when they say 'we'll get back to you'. I just keep drawing for myself anyway and most of my jobs seem to come through friends.

RECENT AND UPCOMING WORK.

I have just completed the illustrations for a board game aimed at getting teenagers to discuss how they feel about issues of gender equality, so I did a lot of undefined pictures of couples. Next I am working on some technical illustrations and a continuing collaboration with a friend. For the past few months we've been setting ourselves colour schemes and then creating big abstract collages and now we need to progress the idea...

Stockholm, Sweden

Two of Hearts for Amelia's Magazine Shelter Card Quilt

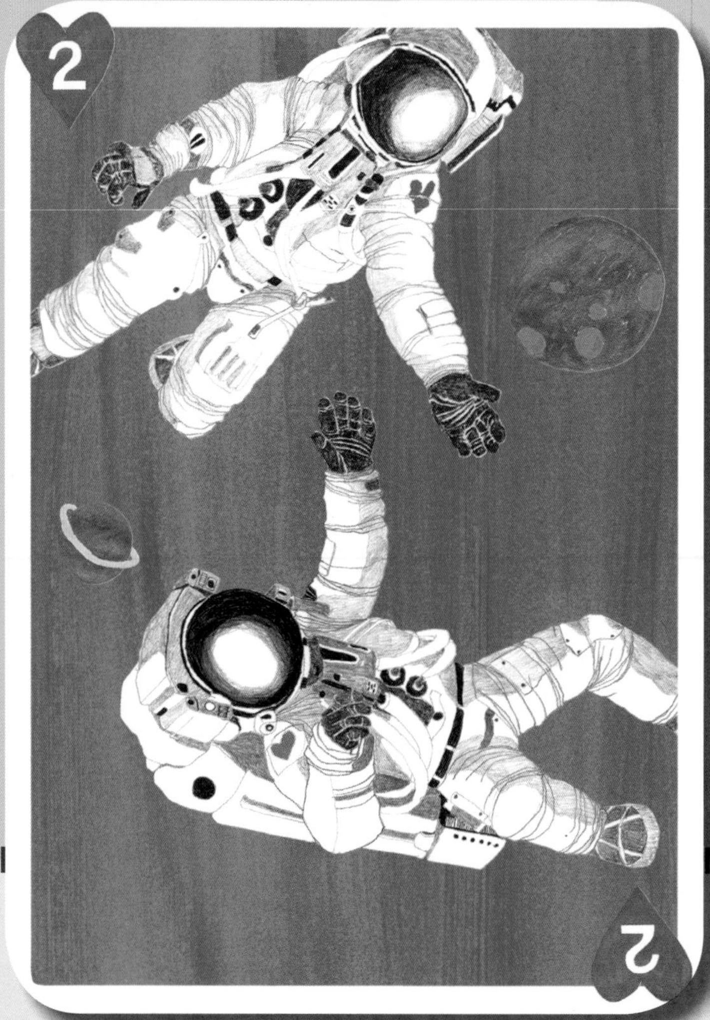

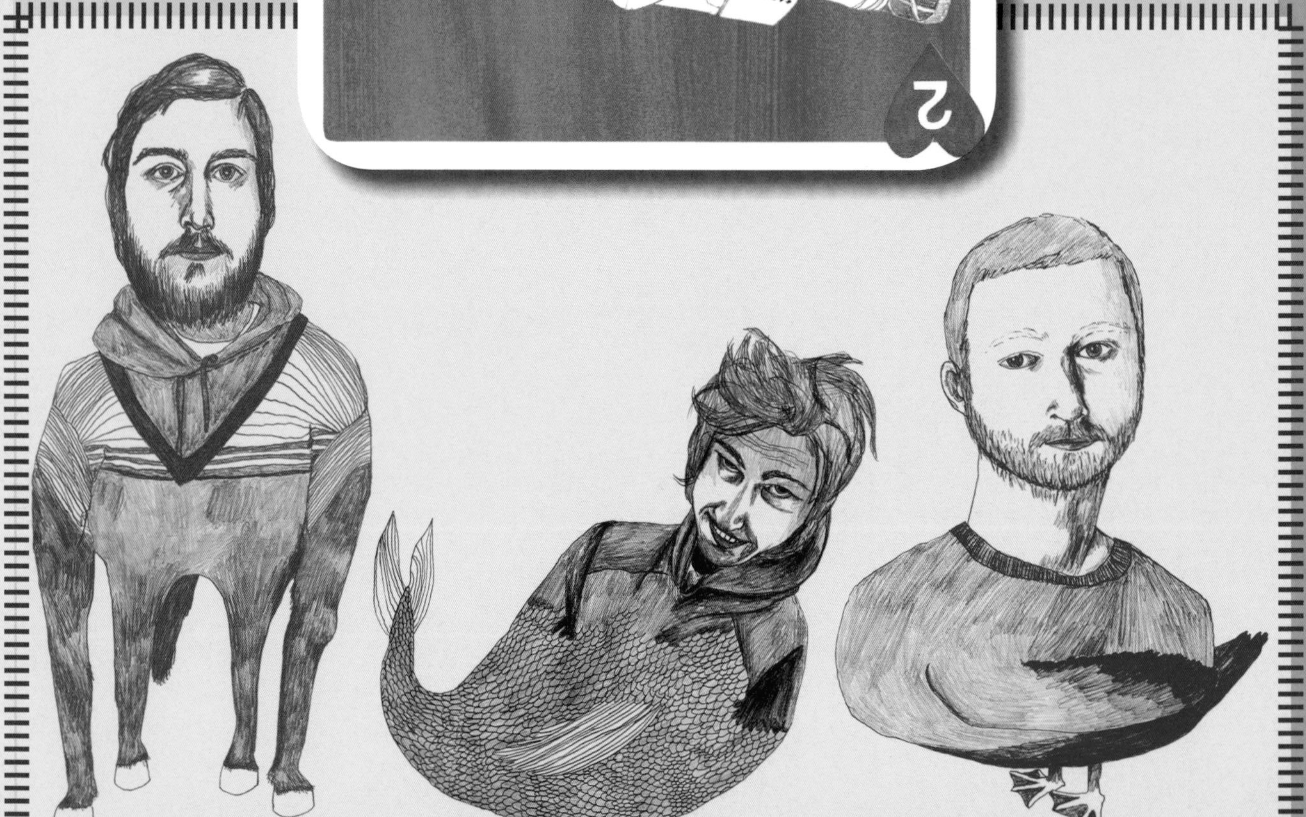

PHOTOVOLTAIC means light-electricity and it is nothing short of miraculous: certain 'solar cells' can actually generate electricity directly from sunshine. Like so many other technologies the photovoltaic effect was discovered by accident, when French physicist Alexandre-Edmund Becquerel was messing around with metal electrodes in 1839. The first solar cell was made from selenium by the American Charles Fritts. It was only 1% efficient.

By the 1950's there was a lot of excitement about photovoltaic solar power for use in space, but its terrestrial use remained limited until the 1970's oil crisis brought about a rapid rise in commercial applications, particularly in small scale items such as calculators and watches. However, despite the passing of several decades, photovoltaic panels have for the most part remained bulky, rigid and costly, preventing their widespread uptake as large scale producers of electricity.

US company First Solar was started by one Harold McMaster, a farm boy turned inventor from Ohio who discovered the secret of manufacturing tempered glass and was dubbed the Glass Genius by Fortune Magazine. After a sunny vacation in Arizona during the 1980's he realised the potential of solar power and set about using his knowledge of glass to develop low cost thin film photovoltaics using cadmium telluride. First Solar has to date installed a total of 74MW of thin film panels on nine sites in the US, and in 2009 it was estimated that they had finally managed to produce power as cheaply as more conventional sources. Right up until his death in 2003, Harold took an active interest in the business, which continues to make great strides in manufacturing large volumes cheaply, principally by going big. Really big. A huge new project has just been announced: a 2GW solar farm will be built over the next few years across 40 square kilometres of the desert near Ordos City, Inner Mongolia, China.

THEREZA ROWE

THEREZA ROWE loves drinking pink strawberry milk in the morning, "it makes my head happy" and she can speak to her rescue cats Kitty and Flash in four languages. She grew up in the beach city of Recife, Brasil. "I spent my childhood catching catfish and bringing them home in the hope they'd become my pets, but sadly they never survived so I had to come to terms with the fact that their home was in the sea and not in my tiny red bucket." A first degree in journalism from her home country was "a big mistake" that led to a second degree in Graphic Information Design at the University of Westminster. Why is illustration referred to as the poor cousin of graphic design, she wants to know. "It's all visual communication, right?"

A problem shared is a problem halved.

My other half is an engineer and he usually comes up with some great practical ideas which I eventually visualise and translate into an illustration. In the case of this brief he showed me the Odysseus solar powered plane which I thought looked magnificent, and the illustration progressed from there. I imagined how a whole town could be powered by photovoltaic solar panels with the Odysseus flying above.

Solar power and capitalism.

It was a challenging subject to explore but it appealed to me because I hear so much about climate change. It was fun to research and translate the information about solar voltaic power into an illustration. It could provide huge amounts of power but its full potential has yet to be explored which left me wondering whether this is due to the lack of long term investment in a capitalist society that prioritises short term gains.

Geometric shapes and laboratories.

My development of an idea changes depending on the project but for the solar voltaic illustration I created the drawing bit by bit by building on preliminary sketches. Usually my work evolves from sketchbooks, which are a container for my ideas, a laboratory for experimentation. Drawing is mixed with hand lettering and collaged found materials such as old envelopes. I love the feel of paper, especially when it carries someone else's story that can feed into an illustration. Much of the time I attempt to convey human actions and emotions through imaginary creatures. I love the power of bold geometric forms combined with colour, but I also tend to rely on happy accidents as a direct result of playing around.

Networking and self-motivation.

It's really important that I love what I do, because passion comes through in each piece of work I produce and keeps me going when times are tough. As an illustrator I have two jobs which I have somehow to balance smoothly and I have a short attention span so it takes a high dose of self-discipline to keep on top of both. One is the fun part, which is drawing, and the other is the hard part; promoting myself and looking for work by networking with peers and potential clients.

Self promotion in practice.

I like to experiment with formats that don't look mass-produced so I am making round-cornered postcards that look like playing cards and I'm in the process of putting together a mailer full of goodies to post out to a few selected art directors and pub-

lishers, which will include a keyring and a con-
certina booklet. My website is always kept up to
date with nicely presented images and I keep a
blog which attracts a fair number of visitors.

Blogging around the world.

Blogging is an amazing tool for the contemporary illustrator. It enables me to engage
with the design community and keep track of
my own process and development. My blog is
a sort of e-sketchbook where I regularly post
stuff that inspires me, also works in progress:
it is a space where 'my readers' get a pretty
good insight into how my head works. It's also
a joy to give and receive instant feedback from
such a great community. I have a Flickr account
where I upload most of my work and have made
hundreds of contacts from around the world. It
is just wonderful to inspire and be inspired by
such talented people.

London, Pedro Almodovar and the Surrealists.

Daily life can be quite isolating because I work
alone, so I always have music in my work
space, anything from Ben Folds to Motorhead
depending on my mood. I feel really lucky to be
living in London because it is such a rich city in
terms of visual culture; if I'm feeling a bit stuck
I take a quick trip into the city just to observe
things and then I come back to work renewed
and inspired. I carry a camera and a Moleskine
with me at all times so that I can document
things that interest me, wherever they are. I
like Pedro Almodovar's films for their unexpected storylines, pop culture references, bold
colours and crazy characters. It would be unfair
to pick a favourite because he portrays all the
women characters and their neuroses with such
raw beauty. Through Almodovar's films I found
the Surrealists, and fell in love with the way
they celebrate chance, experimentation and
freedom. Joan Miró and Antoni Gaudi had such
a fearless childlike approach. I have a surreal and
extremely hyperactive head so drawing provides
me with an excellent outlet to express the world
as I see it.

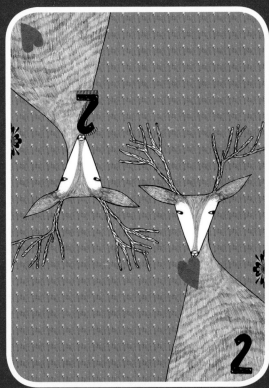

Two of Hearts for Amelia's Magazine Shelter Card Quilt

SWAP

SWAP
TILL
YOU
DROP

WOWZA

Amelia's Magazine, Earth Section

WIND CITY

IT is becoming more essential than ever to design urban buildings that take full advantage of the elements to create energy for their inhabitants. Tall skyscrapers are especially well placed to take advantage of the wind and sun, either through careful retrofitting or by ensuring that intelligent design is implemented right from the start.

Some architects are dreaming especially big. In 2008 the Bahrain World Trade Centre was completed, featuring twin towers linked via three strong bridges holding huge 29m wind turbines that are able to provide up to 15% of the electricity requirements for the building. The bold sail design of the towers acts as a funnel to gain maximum advantage from the winds blowing off the Persian Gulf, and the centre has fast become an icon for urban renewable energy. Of course there are many potential problems with incorporating wind turbines into a building: the noise and vibration of the wind turbines is likely to be extremely loud and could cause structural damage, never mind that

this area is particularly prone to dust storms that could get into the machinery. In most locations it would not be suitable to channel the wind, yet over in the USA comes the promise of integrated wind turbines for the Aquarius Tower in the city of Atlanta and architect David Fisher proposes a Dynamic Tower for that well known bastion of sustainability, Dubai. 420m tall, the 80 floors of this building would each be capable of independent rotation. But better still, there would be a turbine sandwiched between each floor to generate all the energy the building needs (and it's going to need a lot, what with all that rotating). How this could work in reality is not entirely clear.

None of these megastructures appear to consider sustainability beyond the renewable generation of some proportion of their energy, which will most likely be gobbled up by the huge numbers of air conditioning units and other energy sapping gimmicks such as rotating floors. Many other architects all over the world are proposing green skyscrapers that not only incorporate wind and solar technologies, but also agricultural and biogas energy (in the case of La Tour Vivante in France) and even complete sustainability in the case of Vincent Callebaut's somewhat more fanciful 132-storey Dragonfly complex for Rhode Island shaped, you got it, just like a dragonfly's wing. Given that the vast majority of the world's population now lives in urban areas, there is surely something to learn about micro generation and food growing close to where people live and work. After all, it worked for Cuba when they ran out of oil, albeit in a much more low-tech manner.

TRAINED as an interior designer many years ago at Cardiff University, Wynne James has only recently reappraised his first true love: illustration. For now, he spends his days drawing up splendid visions of building interiors for the global architectural firm HOK. One day, someday in the future, he hopes to spend more time with his own ideas.

"I get the most enjoyment from drawing up initial concepts," he explains. And anyway, most clients prefer to see his thinking on good old-fashioned paper. Computers were not abundant when Wynne was trained, and consequently he was able to carry on working in a style learnt from school which involved gouache and pencil, media with which he is still comfortable. He is methodical in laying out his workspace before commencing on a piece of artwork. "It will inevitably descend into an ordered chaos, but the board I'm working on will need to stay clean with all materials carefully managed. The eye of the storm maybe?" His perfect pencil case carries a variety of fine black liners, old BIC yellow ballpoints, Staedtler and Derwent Cumberland drawing pencils and a classic putty rubber. "And a good quality watercolour paper is a must, for me to feel confident and comforted."

In the past a specialised team of illustrators were responsible for all architectural visuals, but during his time in the industry Wynne has watched everything speed up. "With the advent of computers most graduates have lost those hand drawn skills," he sighs, "but it's still important to be able to draw intuitively and computers can really limit how you design." The paradox being that using a computer can get in the way of creativity. "I'm a bit of a luddite," he confesses. "Computer-generated images can appear very clinical." He worries that buildings designed by the likes of architects Frank Gehry – who stretch the latest technologies to create spaces because they can, rather than stepping back to think creatively – are losing the human element in design. "It's possible to win competitions with an amazing model, but is it an effective space to move through?" he questions.

Illustration had a profound effect on the young Wynne. "I guess it's quite common for young children to be more entranced by beautiful and beguiling drawings than by the accompanying words." Along with the usual children's favourite bear characters he was particularly affected by Hedgehog in the Fog, an animation produced by Yuri Norstein in 1975. "It encompasses more craft, detail, warmth, imagination, humour, intensity and creative brilliance than any of the others combined. Wonderfully crafted with clever use of glass to add depth and movement and, a beautiful tale." Perhaps it is no surprise that an interior designer like Wynne should also be influenced by artists interested in physical structure and social commentary. The work of Russian constructivist El Lissitzky and German painter George Grosz are singled out for specific praise whilst contemporary artist Thomas Demand "makes impressive photographed sets that show immense detail and beautiful composition."

Wynne was taught that form follows function, by tutors who went on to become founding members of Centre for Alternative Technology in Wales, so it is perhaps surprising that he has not heard of permaculture. "When we're designing buildings we have to think holistically about the connection to the outside, we consider views and exterior landscaping even when the architects don't ask for this." In his rendition of a multifunctional sustainable tower block he found an appealing idea. "I wanted this mini community to have everything in one place, so the chickens on the roof are sold in the shop on ground floor." He found it easiest to answer the brief as though he was working for an imaginary client, and seems to have chanced on the theories of permaculture through his own common sense.

In another drawing giant waving hands rotate in the wind. "This was an abstract look at the kinetic energy in journeys," explains Wynne. Inspired by the film The Power of Community – How Cuba Survived Peak Oil, the illustration Say Hello, Wave Goodbye portrays a landscape that makes use of underused urban spaces.

"There are huge quantities of wind and wave power around the UK and it's quite criminal that we don't make more use of them." The word 'wave' has been subverted so that the wind creates an emotive gesture. "These are, Side to Side (the Hello), Up and Down (the Bye, Bye), and Rotate and Swivel (the Regal)."

It would be safe to say that Wynne's worries about the environment have evolved over the years – at college he was encouraged merely to be as expressive as possible without worrying too much about the consequences. "It's an inherently wasteful industry. Sometimes we really have to push our clients to deal with sustainable issues." Wynne helped to design a house that was erected in Trafalgar Square as part of the London Green Homes scheme. He is particularly concerned about our waste of water. "We don't think enough about it in Britain, but we need to conserve water." He thinks that legislation to force companies to reduce waste might be necessary although it seems to be easier to offer individuals incentives in their homes.

At least, with the recession, there are more refurbishments happening in preference over new builds. "We have to know where everything is produced, what components can be recycled, what happens at the end of the lifecycle?" It is now commonplace to consider where materials are sourced from, "so for instance – take a chair – we always check whether the wood is FSC rated, or where its content comes from. We have to trace it back [down the supply chain] because companies are prone to bend the truth." How so? "If something says it was manufactured locally that could just mean that it was assembled locally from parts that come from all over the world, or that a final coating has been applied locally... or locally could mean from Holland or Scotland or France, which are all within a 500 mile radius." Cheeky buggers!

THE MAG WIND turbine uses the Savonius design that was invented by the Finnish designer Sigurd J. Savonius in 1922. Looked on from above the blades make an S-shape, which helps them to scoop the air up with less drag. But the most exciting feature of this device is the use of magnetic levitation, whereby powerful magnets are used to suspend a vertical axis wind turbine on a cushion of air, reducing friction, vibration and noise.

Enviro Energies of Ontario was started by Jim Rowan, following some experimenting with tinfoil and a pie dish at his kitchen table one afternoon. The Mag Wind turbine was born to take advantage of the gusting eddies that hit rooftops, and Jim claims that even at very low rotation speeds it can generate more electricity than a normal turbine. Plus it's so kind to the birds (of great importance to Americans, where big wind farms have disturbed habitats) that a hawk reportedly rides atop one of the test turbines. His designs have already captured the imagination of American actor and activist Ed Begley, who turns up at Hollywood events on his bike (Go Ed!) and has ordered a turbine to power his own home.

However, there is word of a much bigger magnetically levitated turbine. In 2007 the ginormous MagLev wind turbine was announced to great fanfare and some extraordinary claims. It is claimed that one single huge MagLev turbine could deliver 1GW, enough to power a small city, whilst taking up a fraction of the land required by conventional wind turbines. And a helicopter could even land on its rooftop (a very important fact of the promotional video, though why this should be necessary is unclear). No concrete information has been released concerning the development of the MagLev.

There is one obvious drawbacks to both ideas – whilst being incredibly simple, the Savonius shape is also amongst the least efficient of wind turbine designs. For this reason it is often used where cost and reliability is more important than efficiency, for example in the twisting advertising signages outside a corner store that are designed to draw the customer in. But just possibly the Savonius design has been wrongly maligned, and one day we will see MagLev turbines the size of pyramids towering above city skylines.

MagLev Magnetic Wind Turbine

Everything is Connected for Amelia's Magazine issue 10

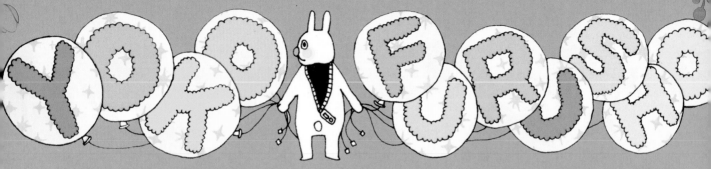

Yoko has a black belt in karaoke.

I was born in Tokyo and my life in Japan was really fun. As a high school student I went to karaoke everyday after school and sang embarrassing Japanese rock songs. I have such good memories of hanging out with my friends in the Shibuya area late into the night, eating beef-bowl (a fast-food dish), talking about our dreams...

Yoko moved to the Big Apple when she was a student.

I wanted to study abroad when I was a high school student, so I decided to come to New York. When I got here I was so nervous because I didn't know anybody and didn't know where to live. I cried a lot! But then I went to college and met many, many good friends, so New York is my second home now. I really like life here because I can really feel all the different people and cultures. Funnily enough this makes me feel more proud of my nationality than I would have done if I had stayed in Japan.

Moving to America made Yoko appreciate Japanese art.

It's embarrassing to say but I had never really looked at Japanese art until I came to New York. Then I realized how great Japanese animation is and how beautiful Japanese woodcuts are. I like how great woodcut masters use so many small pattern details on kimono designs. They inspire me a lot even though my illustration is very different in style.

Yoko's family don't mince their words.

They are my harshest critics! They are like "Yoko, you should do something more like this" or "you must see this exhibition to make better work". But at the same time they are my sweetest advisers.

Yoko likes to mix it up.

I try to mix reality with fantasy in my work. I like to draw small details on hair and clothes and I put textures on imaginary monsters. There is always a main character in my drawings, a reflection of myself in an imaginary world; she is me but she is not me at the same time. My pieces are mostly made by hand with ink and acrylic first, then I add some parts in Photoshop. I'm a full time illustrator now and I'm sharing a studio with friends from school. It took one and a half days to finish my illustration of the MagLev wind turbine, but usually I can finish a piece in a day.

Yoko knows how to party.

When I'm not drawing I hang out with my friends in the East Village near where I live. There are cute cafes and boutiques, movie theatres and good restaurants around here. But the best things are the music shows at the Mercury Lounge, Bowery Ballroom, and Irving Plaza. I like electronic and rock music the most but I'm open to hearing every kind of music. I recently went to see Animal Collective, Efterklang, Cornelius and Shugo Tokumaru.

Yoko has designed her own 'ecology bag'.

I'm aware of environmental issues. People try not to use a plastic bag from the supermarket in Tokyo these days so there is a trend to carry a fabric bag. When the bags are cute more people want to carry them; I went back for a vacation recently and was very happy to see that most Japanese people are carrying an 'ecology bag' now, so I was pleased to be asked to design one. In Tokyo it is even normal to carry your own chopsticks instead of using disposable ones. I hope more people will do similar things elsewhere.

Yoko wants you to face the reality of global warming.

Everybody knows about global warming but they don't react. I put the melting earth inside two heads to illustrate the fact that people know about this serious issue, but the eye masks illustrate the fact that they try not to face it. For the main picture I tried to make the image of the wind turbine really warm because I want people to get a good feeling about new ways of producing energy. It would make me really happy if I could make people feel something positive about earth-friendly technologies.

Yoko is open to what the future will bring.

There is no end goal in my dreams. I'm really happy having fun collaborating with other people, doing something that I really like. So I just hope I will keep having more fun.

261

Want to know more about some of the briefs featured in this book?
Read on:

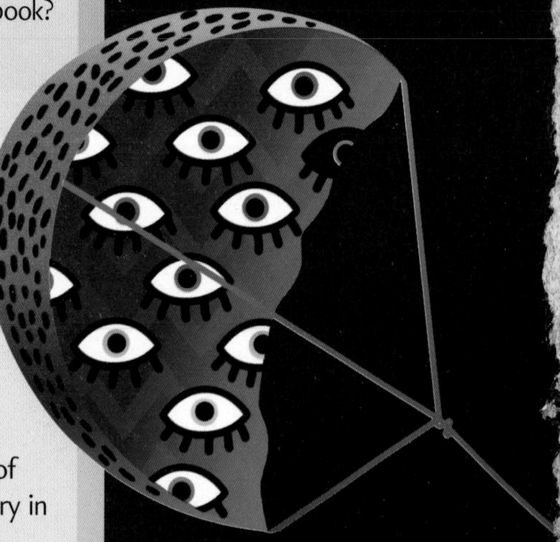

ROYAL BANK OF SUSTAINABILITY FOR C WORDS

Together with the arts activist and campaigning organisation Platform I put together a brief to re-envision the Royal Bank of Scotland as the Royal Bank of Sustainability. In 2008 this big British bank was bailed out by the taxpayer to the tune of many millions of pounds and yet it carries on investing heavily in the fossil fuel industries, so Platform launched a legal challenge against the government to try and make sure that public money used for bailouts is put towards building sustainability. The best ten entries were shown as part of C Words: Carbon, Climate, Capital, Culture at the Arnolfini gallery in Bristol in late 2009.

TWO OF HEARTS SHELTER CARD QUILT

In 2009 the housing charity Shelter asked a host of artists to make artworks inspired by a pack of cards, used in their advertising campaign to show the fragility of a stable homelife for many people. I was given the Two of Hearts to illustrate and I chose 54 of the best submissions to put together in a patchwork quilt – the ultimate symbol of a safe and cosy home. The resulting artwork was exhibited alongside works by Damien Hirst, Vivienne Westwood and many other art world luminaries. It raised £2200 at auction.

CLIMATE CAMP

I first went along to Climate Camp at Heathrow in 2007, and created a poster to promote the London neighbourhood at Kingsnorth, Kent in 2008. In 2009 I put together an open brief to create promotional imagery for the Climate Camp that was held on Blackheath in London. It asked illustrators to tackle the theme of sustainable living whilst taking direct action against the underlying economic system that is causing climate change. The resulting imagery was used on posters, leaflets and stickers, and has been adapted by many other Climate Camps that are springing up across the world.

thanks for reading this book